ESSENCE SPIRIT BLOOD AND QI

MONKEY PRESS takes its name from the Monkey King in 'Journey to the West', the 16th century classical novel by Wu Chengen. The story narrates the bringing of Buddhist scriptures to China; a journey which involves many misadventures and opportunities for learning. The incisive observations of Monkey are humorously contrasted with the sometimes misplaced compassion of Tripitaka the monk under his protection. Monkey blends vision, wisdom and insight with irreverence and mischief.

ESSENCE SPIRIT BLOOD AND QI

Claude Larre and Elisabeth Rochat de la Vallée

transcribed and edited by Caroline Root

MONKEY PRESS

© Monkey Press 1999

CHINESE MEDICINE FROM THE CLASSICS:

ESSENCE SPIRIT BLOOD AND QI

Claude Larre and Elisabeth Rochat de la Vallée

ISBN 1 872468 18 7

Text Editor: Caroline Root

Production and Design: Sandra Hill

Calligraphy: Qu Lei Lei

AcuMedic CENTRE
101-105 CAMDEN HIGH STREET
LONDON NW1 7JN
Tel: 020 7388-6704/5783
info@acumedic.com   www.acumedic.com

Printed on recycled paper by Spider Web, London

CONTENTS

FOREWORD

'Fulfilling one's destiny is just guiding one's life with essences and spirits and *qi* according to the great rule of cosmic animation as expressed in oneself.'

Essences, spirits, blood and *qi* are the fundamental and indispensible elements comprising life in a human being. Their individual qualities and their interactions one with another determine the pattern for all movements of life, mirroring those of the cosmos. By virtue of these constituents within us we are completely integrated with the universal life of heaven and earth. We cannot be disconnected from the natural phenomena which surround us. Nor is our spiritual life separate from the physicality of our environment.

This book explores these ideas, considers each of the substances and presents the authors' insights and observations rooted in scholarship and philosophical reflection. What unfolds is the perception of an individual life in which essences, spirits, *qi* and blood constantly enfold and entwine each other, creating in that process the intricate mechanisms with which we can maintain our vitality, and composing the shape, colour and texture of our destiny.

'The movement of life is nothing other than the perpetual desire to remain alive and produce life'.

Caroline Root
Rhodes 1999

COUPLES IN CHINESE MEDICINE

Elisabeth Rochat: Before the study of essence, spirit, blood and *qi* (*jingshen xueqi* 精神 血氣) as such, we will look at the presentation of couples in Chinese medicine in general. Reality itself is indivisible, but through the presentation of a couple or a dual expression the Chinese have tried to describe precisely where movement exists, where pathology exists, and how to treat it. The movement of life which is reflected in the animation and physiology of mankind mirrors that of cosmic life. This means that the same patterns and laws which make life in the universe also make life in an individual living being. That is the reason why there is a kind of community of life, a kind of resonance from one being to another, and it is also the reason why when analogies are made in the medical texts to such things as heaven and earth or rain and clouds, they are not exactly images, they are more than that, they are descriptions of the fundamental movements of life. We can find these same movements within the human organism, even if they are with certain particularities and specificities for the human species. It is the same for plants and animals, and even for the life of the earth itself, with its rivers and streams. Some texts make comparisons between the rivers on earth and the movement of blood and *qi* (*xueqi* 血氣). But it is not merely a comparison, it is the same thing, the same movement that is seen in the cosmos and in the individual.

It is quite difficult to speak of such generalities as *yinyang* (陰陽), heaven and earth, and *jingshen* (精神), and of what their meaning as couples is in Chinese medicine. So before giving an analysis of some of the characters used in medical texts, I prefer just to read and discuss some quotations from the first chapters of the Nei jing.

'From ancient times, communication with heaven, the trunk of life, has been rooted in *yinyang*.' Su wen chapter 3

The meaning of this quotation is that as a living being, what is essential in my life and what maintains me in my life is a relationship with heaven. This relationship with heaven is not only external, for example through respiration, it is also my ability to create and restore in myself those heavenly qualities which I have in my heart through the presence of the spirits. This is the real trunk of life which is behind the differentiation of *yinyang*. Reading the beginning of Huainan zi chapter 7 there is the same idea, but just expressed in other terms.

'In antiquity, before heaven and earth even existed,
There were only images without forms,
Profound, opaque, vast, immobile, impalable and still.
There was a haziness, infinite, unfathomable, abysmal,
A vast deep to which no one knew the door.

'Then two spirits born together,
Rule heaven and regulate earth.
Deep-like indeed!
No one could see where they ended.
Great-like indeed!
No one knew where they ceased.

'Thereupon they distinguished into *yin* and *yang*,
And quartered the eight poles.
Hard and soft mutually completing each other
The 10,000 beings acquired form.'

Communication with heaven is the real trunk of life which is behind the differentiation into *yin* and *yang*, and this expression *yinyang* as a couple is the first requirement of all sorts of exchanges and compositions which make living beings. But all the conditions of the harmonious composition of a couple always rely on something deeper and more important, here expressed as the relationship and communication with heaven. In other texts it is expressed as free communication with the *shen* (神). The *shen* should be the ultimate regulators of all the movements of life, of everything which is *yin* and *yang* and all their interplay inside the body.

'In the space between heaven and earth, inside the six junctions, the *qi* of living beings, in nine territories and through nine orifices, in five *zang* (臟) and through 12 relays of animation, all communicate with the *qi* of heaven.'
Su wen chapter 3

Between heaven and earth there is an exchange because heaven is made with a rising and expanding movement, and the earth is composed from that which gradually descends and condenses because of the removal of the light and subtle elements for heaven. Therefore there is always a relationship between heaven and earth and they are never separate. There is always communication and exchange, and in this place of exchange which is also the median void, or the space between heaven and earth, we have the mixing of *yin* and *yang*. Here the 10,000 beings and all living beings appear. They are always subject to dual relationships because they have something from earth and something from heaven, and because everything appears by the effect of duality. What belongs to earth, as far as man is concerned, is the bodily structure, and what belongs to heaven is the *jingshen*, the spirits depending on the subtle essences for their expression. But a human being is always the mixing of these two fundamental parents, heaven and earth. In classical texts they are also named as father and mother. This is not just an image, because we really are in the likeness of the exchange between heaven and earth, and we are formed through all the exchanges between particular aspects of heaven and earth. Each living being is at a precise crossing point and dependent upon a lot of agencies determining its exact nature and composition. It is, in other words, his destiny, because he has to follow his nature.

In this space between heaven and earth, all this animation is lived through a human being with a physical organization in the likeness of this great exchange of *qi*. What is important for man is that he has an important quality of belonging to heaven depending on the *jingshen.* His life is really completed in his relationship with heaven or with what he is able to do with the heaven within him. This is why we find in treatment, and it is also said in a lot of classical texts, that if you do not go to the spirits you cannot really treat and you cannot radically cure. All life is ruled by this centre and it is also the very specific efficiency of needles that they can give a signal to the spirits of man, and perhaps first clear the way in order to make this communication and this signal perceptible and possible. So the nine territories, nine orifices and five *zang* just summarize this total similarity between the organization of life in a human being and of life between heaven and earth where this human being exists.

'The *yang qi* is like the sun in heaven. When it loses its place, life is broken and the being no longer shines. Whether the heavenly influx is regularly distributed depends on the solar radiance; thus the *yang* soars upwards and ensures the defence of the exterior.' Su wen chapter 3

Because of the preceding explanation we can understand that to say the defence or the defensive *qi* within the human body is like the sun in heaven is not just a poetic image but is really the best explanation of the movement and the quality of that defensive *qi* inside the body. It is just this likeness which is acting, and it is something in my life which is acting like the movement of the sun in heaven.

What is the sun? The sun is light, warmth, and the rhythm of life because of day and night. In man there is something which is surging from the original and invisible depths like the sun at dawn. Ling shu chapter 18 says it surges from the lower heater. The movement, vitality, warmth and animation expand up to the limits of my body, to the layers of the skin, but they also make clouds and rain. These are due to the warmth of the sun vapourizing the humidity of earth. The clouds can also impregnate the earth by rain. So what is the defensive *qi* within the human being other than that, because it also creates circulation and humidity inside the human body up to the extremities? This is possible because there is vapourization and transportation of these liquids incorporated with a gentle warmth, so that there is an effect of defence at the level of the flesh and at the layers of the skin. It is because of this that a pore can open and close regularly. And it is certainly because of this fire in the lower heater and the impregnation of the vapour and liquids at the level of the lower heater that the defensive *qi* is linked with the lower heater in order to create all the circulation and transportation, thus making the efficiency of the defence.

This is also the way by which the defensive *qi*, during the day, expands the animation inside the bone articulations and gives strength to the muscles, causing the opening of the eyes and the impregnation of the sense organs in order for them to be in relationship with the exterior. During the night there is a kind of coming back, exactly mirroring the sun; a withdrawal to the interior in order to restore the quietness and purity of the essences within the *zang* as well as to renew the proper forces of the defensive *qi*. And you know that this quietness and purity of essences offering support for the spirits are also the best defence a man can have. If the spirits are really determining all the movement of liquids and *qi*, of defence and nutrition and of blood and so on, the best way to have a good defence is to be at peace in the interior. We know that not to be at peace is a good way to get a disease. Of course, this is also the way by which this defence acts during the night in the interior. It cleans and gives strength to the *zang*, and these are very precise functions because defence is not a concept, it is a series of very definite mechanisms, circulations and activities.

'That which gives life to the *yin* is rooted in the five tastes (*wu wei* 五 味) and the five residences (*wu gong* 五 宮) of the *yin* are attacked by these five tastes.' Su wen chapter 3

This is a way to say that what is *yin* is just the reconstruction or the maintaining of the fabric of life, the food and nourishment, the five tastes. What are called the essences of posterior heaven are the way essences are renewed in me. By these essences we rebuild all kinds of liquids, blood, *qi*, and animation, and we transform bodily structure by inner penetration, mixing and so on. If something is really very wrong in these five tastes, in the way we are renewing essences within the body, eventually something will be wrong in the interior at the level of the *zang*, and that will ultimately be an attack on the *jingshen*, at the supreme and highest level of life.

'*Yin* is that which stores the essences (*cang zang* 藏 臟) and then there is a springing up and development (*qi qi* 起 亟). *Yang* is that which defends on the exterior (*wei wai* 衛 外) and then solidity (*gu* 固) is the result.' Su wen chapter 3

What is interesting is that in this quotation we have the dual relationships. If we have to give a definition of *yin* and *yang* it is more exact to make a presentation with the effect of one upon the other. There is always enough *yin*, enough humidity and descending movement, in heaven to make a movement towards the earth, and to give to the earth by means of rain and so on. And there is always enough clarity and purity inside the earth to be able to vapourize and rise up to heaven and make clouds. If it is like that in a living being too, then it is the same as heaven and earth. The essences that are the basis and foundation of life are kept carefully and actively by means of and within the *zang*, they are not kept for themselves, but for the realizing of something. They are to be the support of the springing up, and the *yang* movement. There is no *yang*, no *qi* and no defence if there is nothing to support this movement and to make a firm basis for its springing up. This presentation of the *yin* is important for the storing of the essences, and as the condition necessary for the release and the support of the *yang* movement.

The *yang* movement is of course very important for making the defence of the exterior, but what is also important is to preserve the vitality in the interior of the body, and we can see that in the couple *xueqi*. Everywhere the *yang qi* acts not only like the effusion of something but also as the limits of this diffusion. It is like a current of water which causes the circulation of the water, but also pushes it in a particular direction. This is the most important point, the harmonious composition. If there is not enough essence or *yin* there is no real power in the *yang*. In the first instance you can have a kind of bursting out, but it does not last. After that you just see the end. If there is not enough strength in the *yang* or the *qi* or the animation, it is not only a weakness of *qi* but also a diminution of the presence and power of the essences. For instance, if they are not able to make the transformation needed for the assimilation of new essences, the power of the essences diminishes. It is always like that when you have the expression of animation and vitality in a dual expression, *yin* and *yang*, blood and *qi*, essences and *qi* and so on. The most important thing is how they are able to interplay one with the other in a constant interpenetration. If one is weak we have a series of symptoms, and that always leads to the end of the couple. There is no *yin* without *yang* and there is no defence without nutrition. There is no blood without *qi* and so on. Of course Su wen chapter 3 just emphasizes this by giving very symbolic, sharp examples of this association inside these couples.

'When *yin* cannot dominate *yang* the *mai* (脈) flow violently and precipitately, a disharmony that leads to madness. When *yang* cannot dominate *yin* the *qi* struggles inside the five *zang* and there is no longer communication through the nine orifices.' Su wen chapter 3

In this quotation 'dominate' is *sheng* (勝) and the meaning is to be strong and to take advantage and overpower. So there is something which is unable to ensure all the circulation of vitality and exchange through to the exterior coming from the five *zang*.

Claude Larre: My feeling is that it is not that the *yin* is really dominating, but that it is strong enough not to be overpowered by the *yang*. The *yang* has to be contained in a way, like a river. If the *yin* in a river was too dominating it would no longer be a river, it would be a pond. But if the *yin*, the embankment which is that solid part which channels the water, was not there then the *yang* would be so out of control that it would no longer be of use for any work. So when they say 'dominate' it means to dominate to the point of being able to retain the good value. It is not exactly to dominate, it is to be able to influence to the point where the *yang* is controlled. It is not easy for the *yin* to dominate the *yang* without suppressing the *yang*.

Elisabeth Rochat: This domination is like the controlling cycle of the five elements, it is exactly the same, and the same character, *sheng* (勝). The domination is just to be able to maintain the balance. If to dominate is to restrain, if there is not enough *yin*, not enough liquids in the stomach for example, this would lead to inflammation and dryness, and madness is even one of the possible eventual symptoms of that. The same thing is true for the contrary, because if there are not enough essences to satisfy and fulfil the *zang* there is a kind of agitation which is not circulation, because without power and foundation the *qi* does not follow its normal course. There is just a kind of bursting or an agitation. But this is not because the *yang* is too strong, or the *yin* is weak. The *qi* is just following the same way. There is a disorder, and the disorder is that it is unable to know what the correct way is. This is a kind of blockage due to the *qi*. For instance, you can have this kind of blockage due to obsessive thoughts having an effect on the *qi* of the liver. Other examples of this are from a lack of or poor quality blood of the liver, or a lack of the essences and liquids coming from the spleen.

At the innermost place there is the heart or the five *zang*. This is the centre, the home of the spirits, because that is the real origin of life. All our life is ruled from this centre, and it is the beginning of the building of a structure to be made with bones, liquids and flesh. The first structure is like the form given by earth, but there is always communication from this centre to outside and from outside into the centre. This allows all kinds of entrances and exits. It could be in the form of respiration or alimentation, but it also includes all kinds of knowledge and communication which have an effect on the good balance of the centre. All of this passes through the orifices, and it is one of their main functions to ensure all this communication from the essences and even from the *jingshen*. Something coming from my spirits needs to use essences to be expressed. While I am speaking here I am using my essences to make the *qi* of my voice, to make myself stand using the marrow in the bones of my legs and all kinds of blood for the movement of my muscles. The regulation of activity is made by means of the spirits and essences inside the *zang*, if not, we lose the richness of the interior. If there is breakdown in communication or a weakness in communication between the interior and the orifices, we lose control, and we are unable to use all our organism. We are able to see things or hear things but the objective interpretation might be lost. We cannot transform all these things because of the lack of *jingshen*. There are also, of course, a lot of more physical disorders. It is the great danger of life, not just that there might be something a little bit wrong with my eyes, but that it is a sign, and if I want to treat it I have to start with the richness and quality of the centre.

This being so, the saints behave in accordance with *yinyang*. The muscular forces and the network of animation (*jin mai* 筋 脈) are composed of a single *qi*, bone and marrow are consolidated and strengthened, *qi* and blood flow one with another in a concerted movement. This being so, The result is the harmonious balance of the interior with the exterior (*nei wai* 內 外); the perverse influences cannot cause any harm; the hearing and sight are acute. The *qi* is established in its perfection.' Su wen chapter 3

The muscular forces and the network of animation, the bone and marrow and the *qi* and blood are all examples of this interdependent relationship of couples. I think it is clear that in this situation perverse influences cannot cause any harm. The defence and its strength need not only to have a lot of *yang* but also to rely on quiet, pure and rich *yin.* Now all the relationships between what are called the three treasures, *jing, shen* and *qi* are possible.

Claude Larre: When you go and visit an official in China you go for specific business. You want to be authorized to go somewhere or you want to establish relationships and so on. That takes place on the exterior. But when you enter the office you see the man behind his desk is trying to impress you by his calmness, harmony and composure. There is the balance between the official life and the exterior. You are the exterior. You come and you slightly disturb the man who was guarding himself and all the essences in his *zang.*

When writers insisted on this inner peace they were talking of what they knew, because many of them were educated men but of lowly origins. In our minds, the exterior is usually the physical, and the inner is something very spiritual. It is not exactly like that. I am sure that the refinement of Chinese civilization is so certain and subtle that in their calligraphy or the small bird singing in the corner of the house, this quietness for them is something emanating from their spiritual life. If we just have the inner and the outer, that would be too geometrical. There is a centre, there is a periphery, and there are exchanges between the two, but where are the actual applications of that? The applications might be found anywhere.

'What is essential for *yinyang* comes down to this: solidity (*gu* 固) depends on whether the *yang* are well tightened (*mi* 密).' Su wen chapter 3

Elisabeth Rochat: The meaning of this is that if the periphery of the body is not well regulated by a good rhythm coming from the defence and the *yang*, there is no solidity, and there is no solidity of life if there is no firmness in the behaviour. The vitality can be dissipated easily by things such as perspiration, excitement or emotions.

'A lack of harmonious composition between the two would be like spring without autumn, winter without summer. Such is the rule of the saints.' Su wen chapter 3

Here you see the great rule of all couples, this is the highest level of composition. If we have these three couples, these three interchanges, *jingshen*, *shenqi* and *jingqi*, they are all in dual relationships. They are all in relationships which are to express particulars of the maintenance of life and animation. All of these dual expressions have a particular level of explanation.

Jingshen are something like vital spirits. They are certainly the highest level of human life. Are the *jingshen* visible or not? In a way they are visible, but in what way are they perceptible? By the *xueqi*, for example. There is no colour for the *jingshen*, but there is a right colour for the blood when it is animated by the *jingshen*, giving a good colour to the complexion for instance. This is one of the possible visual aspects of good *jingshen*.

Jingqi operate at the level of the *zang*, with the releasing of the *qi* from stored essences. The essences support this releasing of *qi* and enable the general *qi* of the body to transform and work, to capture new essences and to assimilate them. There is no *qi* without essences to be its foundation, and there are no essences without *qi* to transform and assimilate them. We can also see that there is always a presence behind these essences and *qi*, and it is the power of transformation which is the main characteristic of a living human being. A living being is that which transforms everywhere and at every moment.

Shenqi are the force, the strength, which is also needed for the expression and animation coming from the spirits. This is at the highest level. We can see that in these expressions essences, *jing*, are always in the first position, *qi* is always in the second position, and *shen* is here the first member of the couple and in *jingshen* the second. I do not want to make too much analysis, but we know that it is very obvious to say that *jing* is on the *yin* side and *qi* is on the *yang* side. Or if the *jing* is the best expression of the *yin* and the *qi* is the best expression of the *yang*, *shen* is really behind this *yinyang* differentiation, and able to explain them. Specifically, they are only able to express themselves and make life through the harmonious composition of *yin* and *yang*, through essences and *qi*, and *qi* and blood. This is all an explanation of the last paragraph of Su wen chapter 3.

'But in the case of a too powerful *yang* that cannot be kept tightened, the *yin qi* is interrupted. If the *yin* is steady and the *yang* is well tightened, *jingshen* are controlled (*zhi* 治) as they should be.' Su wen chapter 3

We do not know if they are controlled or if they control. We are forced to choose in English. In fact in reality the *jingshen* are in control of the perfect tension, and in this sense *jingshen* are controlling life too. There is always this kind of feedback effect.

'But if separation and rupture (*li jue* 離 絕) between *yin* and *yang* occur, *jingqi* are interrupted (*jue* 絕).'
Su wen chapter 3

This is the interplay between essences and *qi* making up all kinds of the elements of life. Mentally, spiritually and physically speaking, if there is the beginning of a lack of *jing* and *qi* for the *shen*, then the result is the departure of the *shen* or the loss of the sense of expression of the *shen*, both of which lead to the end of life.

The following quotations from chapter 4 of Su wen are just to remind you that all things, and all operations in a human being may be described through *yin* and *yang*. Behind these names all kinds of balance and relationships are possible.

'When one speaks of *yinyang* in man, the exterior is *yang* and the interior is *yin*. When one speaks of the body of man, the back is *yang* and the abdomen is *yin*. When one speaks of *yinyang* in the *zangfu* (臟府) of the human body, the *zang* are *yin* and the *fu* are *yang*. The back is *yang*: the *yang* within the *yang* is the heart. The back is *yang*: the *yin* within the *yang* is the lung. The front is *yin*: the *yin* within the *yin* is the kidneys. The front is *yin*: the *yang* within the *yin* is the liver. The front is *yin*: the maximum *yin* (*zhi yin* 至 隱) within the *yin* is the spleen. Such are the corresponding relationships of *yinyang*, inward/outward (*biaoli* 表裡), internal/external (*neiwai* 內外), hen/cock (*cixiong* 雌雄).'
Su wen chapter 4

The supreme *yin* is sometimes the kidneys and sometimes the spleen, it depends on the context. Here we have the communication between heaven and earth which is compared with the sun which is in heaven but which comes from the depths of the earth just before dawn. The five *zang* are just the expression of the ascending and descending movement of the sun and all the displays between the clouds and the rain. For instance, the *yang* within the *yang* is the heart, and the heart is here because this is the *yang* movement of diffusion. The heart is called the *tai yang* which is the name of the sun. The lung is the *yin* within the *yang* because it is the upper part of the body, and it has this kind of descending movement making liquids descend down to the bladder and kidneys. If the kidneys are the *yin* within the *yin*, it is because they are the power within the depths. Here we know they are the foundation of any strength. The level which is the *yang* inside the *yin*, which is the rising of the sun or the movement coming from the depths with great power, corresponds to the liver.

In this presentation the turning place in the centre is the spleen, and this is the supreme *yin* because the spleen is here seen in the likeness of the earth which is able to receive everything, and to give birth to anything. This is one of the best qualities of the *yin*. It can receive and transform in order to give back other things. An example is with seeds and grains. The seed is received by the earth and transformed in the depths of the earth, and then all sorts of grains are produced there. This centre is able to make a turning place, with all the movement between rising and descending, between the elevation natural to the spleen and the descending natural to the stomach. So it is in this context, in this place, that the spleen is called the supreme *yin*.

There are also some other couples at the end of this passage: *yinyang*, inside/outside, internal/external and hen/cock. All these are different aspects of *yinyang*. Inside/outside *(biaoli)* is for all of the movements towards the interior or the exterior. Internal/external *(neiwai)* makes the difference between two areas, not only inside and outside the body, but the inner part of the body and the outer part of the body. The difference between internal/external and inside/outside is that internal/external is rather a question of zone, this area compared to that area. Whereas with inside/outside it is about all the movement towards the interior or the movement towards the exterior. Finally, hen/cock is an image of male and female, and the image of production by new composition and mixing. All these are just examples of the precision of the great *yinyang* couple. You have *yinyang* meridians, and *zang* and *fu*, but these meridians are in *biaoli* relationships, and the *zang* could be internal and the *fu* external. But the *zang* and the *fu* could be internal and the meridians could be the external. Or what is outside the body could be external and the internal could be what is inside the body.

JING 精 ESSENCE

Elisabeth Rochat: The character *jing* (精) is made with two parts. On the left is the image of a grain of cereal or rice which is bursting or exploding (米). This is a decomposition of the grain. It could be the bursting of the grain within the earth or inside the stomach for assimilation. The right hand part of the character is the colour of life (青). This is green, or any colour giving the impression that life is circulating well. If you look at vegetation during the spring when the sap is rising, you have this impression, not only of green but of a vivid green. If you look at a man in perfect health with a good complexion, you not only have the vision of the colour on the face, but also behind that very harmonious composition there is the impression of a strong and good vitality. This is also *jing*. It is important to know that colours are not lifeless, but are also what is behind the composition making up the colour. The impression given by the appearance to a practised eye is very important for diagnosis.

Claude Larre: You see photographs, and they are either on matt or glossy paper. When it is glossy you see not only the colour but also the effect of the colour. But that is totally external. You know that the quality of the paper means that the effect was artificially made by the printer. Here, on the contrary, when you see the radiance of the colour, because you are a human being and you are concerned with health, you think that the inner condition of health is so powerful that it shines outside. What is understood is that everybody has a direct feeling of good health which is so powerful that it is possible to see it on the face, especially for those trained in Chinese medicine. The good point about this explanation of *jing* is that the Chinese in their classical books used words which tell of the joy and the life and the shining of things. It is natural in Chinese civilization not to dim the effects. On the contrary, they let them be felt by people and that is the reason why Chinese faces are always full of life. This noisy aspect of Chinese life, especially these days, is just additional testimony of their feeling of life.

This feeling of life is transferred to everything. If it is a plant it will be in this green colour which is no longer just green but the colour of life in nature where plants are concerned. If it was an animal, you would just press your foot onto the body of a pig or any other cattle, to see how much fat was there. This is the sign that they have been nourished with care. For man, all the places on the body where the flesh is round are the places where the blood has been active and is there shining through the skin. Seeing all the range of the Chinese perception of health on the face you see that. They would also insist on the blue-black quality of the hair for men and women.

Elisabeth Rochat: So etymologically speaking, essences are these materials which are able to rebuild life, for instance food and grains, in order to give real animation and sustaining support for animation, and to restore all the aspects of life which can then be seen on the exterior of the body. But more specifically, what are essences, and what is the meaning of this character *jing* in Chinese texts?

We have seen elsewhere that *jing*, even in the couple *jingshen*, can also be translated as light and subtle. This is because if it is an element of my life that I am able to take from another source, then it must be reduced to a very subtle state in order to be able to pass from one pattern of life to another. There is a name for that in Chinese medicine, *jingwei* (精微). The meaning of *wei* is subtle, microscopic, very tiny, very fine. In modern Chinese this character is often used like our 'micro'. *Jingwei* is therefore the intermediate state between the essences composing food, for instance, and those essences which are then attracted into my body by my five *zang* in order to impregnate them. There must be these kinds of very subtle stages, for example in transformation in the breaking down of the proper structure of the food. It is no longer food, it is the vitality of the rice, or all the essences which formerly made up the rice, but no longer with any form. It is through the stomach, which has all the ability to make a new form, that these free essences are now able to compose and to be seized by the power and nature of your own structure, and to make flesh, liquids, cells, hair, thoughts and even the support, basis and manifestation of your emotions.

This is quite important because through that we can have an idea of what essences are. They are elements or components of life, and life is inside these components, and the composition of these essences is the special model for a living being. They are the inseparable elements of life, and if you do separate them then there is no more life. Within these essences the power of life is different depending on the natural structure of the food itself. There is not the same exterior aspect or power of life in rice as there is in meat or fruit. This is all a consideration for how to eat in order to restore the various aspects of life.

There is also another point which is that essences seize one another, embrace and join. This is the distinctive movement of essences, but they need patterns in order to do that. Patterns with rules and norms for life are given at the moment of the conception of a being, because when the being first appears it is by the conjunction of two kinds of essences. The essences of the mother and the father mix and offer each other what is essential. But through them there is also all the lineage and all the circumstance of life, and all the exchanges between heaven and earth. This is clearly said in ancient texts, that I am the child of my parents, and through them I am the child of water and fire, heaven and earth.

When the two essences which constitute the life of two different people, a complementary male and female, seize one another, they make a new composition, and this new composition determines a kind of rule by heavenly effect. This is a rule of development which belongs to the human species and is always the rule for development of the human being as described in the essences of the mother and father. All kinds of details and precision are given by the unique qualities of the essences of this specific man and woman. This is the Chinese understanding. There is a mixing in the original composition of these 'essences of anterior heaven', and this composition must then obey the great law of organization, like heaven and earth, *yinyang* and so on.

Because these essences are inseparable from the rule of organization there is a development of the structure of life. There is development of the body, through the embryo and the fetus making the flesh and blood vessels and organs and so forth. All this is due to the organization coming from the essences. This is the way to use what comes first from the mother and father and afterwards from the exterior world. The latter are the 'essences of posterior heaven', resulting from your own particular transformation of essences from the exterior.

The image of the loom was always present in the mind of an ancient Chinese person. The meaning of the character for meridians, *jing* (經), is the norm or the celestial rule of life. It is also the warp of a loom. When you have a loom, before starting weaving you have fixed vertical threads, and this is the first meaning of this character. It is exactly the same thing in the image of the human being. There is something which is inside us at the very beginning of life, and after that we have a lot of threads, but you also have a pattern to follow. Threads are like essences and we always need more threads to weave the fabric. We also have some kind of motif on the tapestry. This is a life making its destiny with a drawing of this motif. The shining of the colours and their beauty should be an effect of the *jingshen* and the *shenming* which are mysteriously behind the warp and which give the meaning of the weaving with the threads of each of the five colours or five tastes.

In this image there is always movement too. The essences, *qi* and blood are always in a process of transformation, like any kind of expression of these essences in the body. Transformation is the condition of the cooperation of the elements. If there is no transformation there is stagnation and separation within the living body. This is very obvious in the example of the pathology of body fluids. If there is a lack or a weakness in the transformation of the body fluids, little by little there is a condensation of the liquids which are no longer impregnating the tissues and the flesh, but which are separated not only from the flesh and the tissue but also from all the currents of animation and circulation. This leads to pain or to an accumulation of liquids, or to a tumour or to any other kind of disease according to the circumstances. For instance, where there is phlegm the great intention of treatment is to restore the transformative process which is able to eliminate or deal correctly with those liquids which are no longer part of your living body, and that may be the cause of disease.

There is the same process in the mind. The void of the heart is really the ability to take responsibility for all things, and to do that indefinitely. It is also the way to adapt all one's vitality to the rhythm of the universe, to the four seasons and to the exchanges in the environment and surroundings. It is not enough to have efficient transformation, you also have to be able to adapt all that according to the circumstances. You do not have the same defensive *qi* during the winter as during the summer. This is true not only for the defensive *qi* but also for thinking and the will and so on. This is just what is said in chapter 2 of Su wen, 'How to Harmonize according to the Four Seasons'. The four seasons are the four *qi*, following the inspiration of the spirit, or allowing the spirits to guide life.

ESSENCES TASTES AND BODYFORM

'The tastes (*wei* 味) support (*gui* 歸) the body (*xing* 形); the body supports the *qi*, the *qi* supports the essences; the essences support transformation (*hua* 化). The essences are nourished (*shi* 食) by *qi* and the body is nourished by the tastes. The transformations produce (*sheng* 生) the essences and the *qi* produces the body. The tastes injure (*shang* 傷) the body and the *qi* injures the essences. The essences, through transformation, make the *qi* and the *qi* is injured by the tastes.' Su wen chapter 5

Elisabeth Rochat: There is more in this dense text than first appears, but what is important is to see all the interplay of essences, *qi*, body form and tastes. All that is under the control and animation of the special activity of the *qi* which is transformative, and which is always the necessary condition of a good maintenance of any member of a couple or of vitality. We always need to restore to a couple the exchanges and the transformations and processes of life needed to maintain the essences. This is the reason why the anatomy and physiopathology of Chinese medicine are rather different from occidental medicine, because everything is always in process.

Here with the essences there is a kind of earthly aspect, a density even if it is very subtle. Essences are very dense because they are full of life and full of the desire for living.

The desire is just this movement towards each other. If essences are realized they are lead by this movement to bind together and to perpetuate and produce life. The movement of life is nothing other than the perpetual desire to remain alive and create life. This is the bonding of the essences and it is always present at each level, with a particular inner penetration present in the creation of a living being. Each person is a new composition of essences.

Now we can see that essences and *qi* are absolutely inseparable. There is no use for essences without transformation, and transformation is one of the effects of *qi*. There is no *qi* if there are no essences to give birth to and to fix and to sustain it. We can also see that there is no separation possible between the essences of anterior heaven and posterior heaven. The essences of anterior heaven are just the model for the other and for the continuation of the life of my own nature which is a condition of what is called my destiny.

So where are the spirits? They are just here, and nobody knows exactly why they are here or not. If I build something like a welcoming structure then it is just to welcome the spirits. The spirits, like birds, come to this tree or structure, or they do not. If they come a human being develops, with a particularity of essences to be the *jingshen*. It is this which gives the very precise quality of the human being who is able to appeal to heaven and have a way of coming back to heaven. If not there is just a natural abortion. If the spirits are just here, they have to remain and not only remain but remain giving the orientation of life. They give the movement of all circulation and transformation. Thus the spirits are right in the very centre of the person's vitality. The *jingshen* are like the highest level of the expression of human destiny. All the other things, such as all the couples like defence and nutrition or *xueqi*, are the expression of this first condition of life where essences are inseparable from *qi* and act together to build this welcoming structure for the spirits and have to continue to maintain the welcoming aspect of the structure. The welcoming is done by all the circulation and communication, going to and coming from the inspiration of the spirits. And we will see that the *xueqi* is one of the best ways for the spirits to be present everywhere in a man.

Question: Is *jingwei* later called *gu qi* (穀 氣)?

Elisabeth Rochat: It is not exactly the same thing. What is called *gu qi* is the *qi* coming from water and grains (*shui gu* 水 穀), or the liquids and solid food. The meaning of *gu* is cereal, but it is the equivalent of food. In the *jingwei* it is more precise. There is no longer any cereal, there is no name and no form. This is such a subtle state that it can pass into and make another life. Maybe in other books that is called *gu qi*, but it is really a weakening of the classical texts because there are three or four different expressions describing the different stages of assimilation, and in those modern texts there is only one because they prefer to refer to occidental terminology.

We can now understand many of the quotations about essences such as 'essences are the foundation of the being' or 'when two essences come together there is the appearance of what is called spirits'. These two are from Ling shu chapter 8. We can also understand the different levels of the meaning of *jing. Jing* is the living fabric of the universe, the element of life which has to be transformed and put in motion to make all the living beings between heaven and earth. This is the fabric of life, like *qi. Qi* is also everywhere and everything. As an illustration we can take knitting. The wool is the *jing*. The wool makes threads of various colour and thickness. These threads of wool make cloth or a scarf by the alternating and unceasing work of the two needles - these two needles are *yin* and *yang*, and the result is the cloth or the being.

We can call everything essences or *qi*, or the mixing of essences and *qi*. Everything which exists exists by and with essences. This is also seen in chapter 8 of Ling shu. All that exists can only exist because there is *qi*, movement, animation and transformation. In the human being essences are the faithful reproduction of one's own proper nature. This is the original gift of anterior heaven, and the essences are particularly linked to the kidneys. The kidneys represent the origin of life and the ability of life to reproduce exactly from the original model of life. They are the guarantee and the keeper of the pattern of life, in the same way that there must be a pattern for the knitting. At the level of the kidneys, essences are most faithful to themselves and to oneself. They are used to make another life with their richness and power. These are the essences for the reproduction of life, essences of sexuality, and in a man more precisely sperm. We can see that in the form of a liquid it is nothing other than a very rich and dense possibility of making life. This understanding is also the origin of all the different kinds of exercises which use this richness to invigorate an individual life, for instance in certain Daoist practices. But there are also Daoist exercises with saliva, which is another a very rich liquid.

The essences of the kidneys are also the model for the essences of the five *zang*. This allows the five *zang* to produce their own quality of *qi*, in order to invigorate the specific movement of life which they represent inside the body. For instance, the essences of the liver release *qi* which is able to give the springing up of life and to invigorate the circulation towards the exterior. The acid taste is nothing other than essences, incorporated into my body by the *jingwei*, with the specific quality of life and animation inside them which is able to invigorate the movement of life represented in the universe by the wood and in a human body by the liver.

Of course essences are not only the beginning of the process of releasing all the *qi* inside the body, they are also, through transformation and the activity of *qi*, an element of the rebuilding of all the form of my life. They rebuild all the shape that I have. This is done particularly through the liquids and the blood which are transported everywhere to support elements of this rebuilding of the form. The cohesion, the strength to remain together, is given not only by this ability of the essences to join one with another, but also to join with the *qi* and the free circulation which is able to guard and restore these forces. There is a kind of strength in the ability to do that. The strength from the free circulation allows the cohesion. This is the reason why there are always spaces and passages in the muscles and the flesh, as well as in the smallest mass that you can imagine. For example, a cell is a mass, and to remain a cell it must remain open to free circulation. If not there is no more transformation, no more incorporation, and there will be disequilibrium.

Question: Can there be a pathology of essences?

Elisabeth Rochat: It depends what you call essences. If you take essences at the highest level of their character's meaning there is just this kind of element of life ready to be seized by the movement of life itself, and there is no possible pathology. This is the reason why there is no pattern of superabundance as far as this aspect of the kidneys is concerned. There is no pathology of the brain, as the sea of marrow, in chapter 33 of Ling shu, just a pattern of insufficiency. But a superabundance is just long life with good strength of the bones and accuracy of ears and eyes.

I think we can have pathology of essences if something is wrong in a particular form or shape which is produced inside the body. For instance if there are not enough elements given by posterior heaven, for example during childhood, then there would be an insufficiency in growth and development. You can also have weakness in the spirits as well as in the body. But it is not an insufficiency of essences as such, it is just an insufficiency in the ability to renew the essences. You can have pathology linked with essences when they are in the special form of liquids, for instance in the pathology of *jin ye* (津 液), or the pathology linked to rebuilding by the essences. But it is not a pathology of essences as such.

What is the difference? It is that essences have no form and no shape. They are the condition of any shape, they are able to make any and every form or part of our body or mind. It is perhaps because they are so subtle that they have no definite form and that they are able to fully impregnate the *zang*. They are able to match the ability of the spirits and express all the forms taken by the body, but also by knowledge, perception and passion, under the movement and animation given by the *qi*. Pathology can appear only when a shape is delineated or a form is taken. Of course, this depends on the rebuilding and the firmness and strength of the defence. The *qi* which is responsible for defence is also responsible for the condition of nutrition. It is always their breakdown which is the beginning of some kind of trouble or pathology.

ESSENCES AND SPIRIT
JING SHEN 精 神

Elisabeth Rochat: Essences are everywhere because they rebuild bone marrow and the brain in the skull. We understand that this quality of essences and the force with which they are assimilated, incorporated and maintained is the condition of the fullness of the bones or the marrow, or the accuracy of the mind in the brain and so on. When the essences are good they are more able to welcome the presence of the spirits and to support the enlightenment coming from the spirits. This is also called *jingshen*. One effect of the *jingshen* is very obviously on the sense organs in the head. To have good eyes is not only to see colours but also to know the impression given by the colour which is a resonance of the real inner structure and life. This is diagnosis as well as psychology. To have this kind of accuracy in the eyes, you need to have good irrigation by liquids or blood, and a good mechanism and optic nerve in the eyes from the *qi*, but you also need this precise quality of essences able to support the vitality of the spirits giving good assessments and judgments. This is the reason why Su wen chapter 17 has an explanation of *jingming* (精明). *Ming* is the same as in *shenming* (神明), the radiance of the spirits. *Jingming* is the radiance of the essences, which is nothing other than the ability of the essences to welcome the radiance coming from the spirits. *Jingming* is in the head, in the skull, and allows a good functioning of the upper orifices which are the more subtle activities of consciousness and knowledge. Also, it determines the quality of relationships with the outside, with other beings and with all that is exterior. So essences are the support for the strength of the bones, as well as the accuracy of knowledge and perception. If your spirits are present when you make perceptions your perception is just and you know the reality. This is the reason why there is nearly no difference in ancient Chinese between to know and to perceive.

Claude Larre: The difference between man and animals is that animals are presented as having *xueqi* and having *fan qi* (煩 氣), coarse *qi*. Man is said to have *jing qi* (精 氣), refined *qi*. Afterwards he has *jingshen*. When they are talking of *xueqi* they are talking of animated life, nothing more. This is natural for those kinds of living beings in which you never find the clarity, the subtlety or lightness that you find in man's activities of thinking, doing or eating. Man controls his eating, usually, an animal does not. When a man eats his food he knows the food, maybe not as clearly as cats and dogs are able to, but from another angle the spirits of man detect in the food the qualities which are more than the satisfaction of a common appetite. There is even some nourishment for the spirits in what is nourishment for the body. The *shen* is not seen in animals as such, and the presentation of *shen* in animals is that the animals are too coarse to sustain the s*hen*. It is not possible to have *shen* which are not related to heaven and man, because the constitution of *shen* is to have this heavenly origin. But since animals have animation it is normal that the *shen* would use animals too, but more as their mounts than as their selves. It is the same thing in man. You have people who appear to be more animal than man, but still they are men. So pondering over the text of Huianan zi chapter 7 and other texts of Zhuang zi and the way the Chinese are associating animals with spirits, we reach the conclusion that we reserve *shen* for human life. The connection between *shen* and animals is not at the level of the self, it just adds some sort of demonstration to the ability of the *shen* to present themselves specifically.

'*Yinyang* is the way of heaven and earth (*tian di* 天 地), mastercord and mesh (*gang ji* 鋼 紀) of the 10,000 beings, father and mother (*fu mu* 父 母) of change and transformation (*bian hua* 變 化), rooting and beginning (*ben shi* 本 始) of life and death (*sheng sha* 生 殺), residence of the radiant spirits (*shen ming* 神明).' Su wen chapter 5

Elisabeth Rochat: We have here five statements, four expressing *yinyang*. They are inseparable because there is no father without a mother and no mother without a father, and there is no mastercord without mesh, and no mesh without mastercord. This is one aspect of *yinyang*. There is no *yin* without *yang*, and no *yang* without *yin*. Nothing is absolute, because on earth in the human condition it is this mixing, this interplay, which is the condition of life. All is achieved through change and transformation, and even appearance and disappearance, life and death, are just expressions of this great movement of life in which we are caught up.

The fifth proposition is '*yinyang* … is the residence of the radiant spirits'. After the four presentations using dual expressions and couples, this is the way to reach or to show the unity of all of that. Of course there are the essences, the *qi*, the blood, and the nutritive and defensive *qi*, and there are bones and flesh and the lung and spleen and so on. But all of that is for the unity, because life as well as needing diversity and division to express and multiply and reproduce itself, also needs a kind of fundamental unity in order not to err. For instance, the *shenming* visible when your complexion is good allows you to show that unity. The radiance of the spirits is an effect of essences or *qi*, or essences and *qi* or blood, or blood and *qi*, or of nutrition or defence or of what is an expression of the *zang*. You can make a choice. When any kind of separation has occurred and you have a disease, you can make a diagnosis by all these signs and see what is not functioning very well. It is the unity of all that which is manifested in the harmonious composition, and the unity of all that which is behind it which is also due to the active presence of the spirits. Behind all of these couples there is the great unity. I cannot express anything if it is not with a dual expression because as a living being I am definitely in this kind of contradiction and twofold movement of life, and I am also subject to that in my expression and language. The fact of being alive and moving and so on always depends upon a lot of relationships, and also expresses vitally the unity of all that.

Claude Larre: We do not usually pay any attention to the movements we are making. It takes more effort to do things with attention, even if they are small. Zhuang zi chapter 2 says 'when we are born everything goes by itself'. So this question of how what has been explained as a twofold thing is able to compose is not a question, the question is how is it possible that those two things will not make a unique gesture. The pathology is there. What is to be done automatically is digestion, respiration, blood circulation, walking and so on. But if the junction is not made, it may have an effect even as high up as the spirits. The spirits are no longer in control, because the coordination of all this *qi* through the *jing* has to be made at the highest level by the *jingshen*. The *jingshen* is the leader. If the leader is not active or is stopped from exerting his leadership, then everything stops.

Question: Is there a relationship between the essences and the eight extraordinary meridians?

Elisabeth Rochat: No, there is nothing specific. Essences are the basis for existence and the reinforcing of all kinds of meridians and networks of animation, being the substance for the *qi* as well as the blood or liquids. This is the kind of mysterious mixing of *jing* and *qi* which expresses itself in a different form in all the different components of life. The *zang* are fundamentally for work between essences and *qi,* but what are behind that in each *zang* and in the mastery of the *zang* which is made by the heart, are the spirits. An extraordinary meridian is a good renewal of vitality, of forces and currents of animation and of blood and all kinds of elements for nutrition and rebuilding. A meridian is the route for this circulation and for the use of this specific quality inside the territories under its authority. We will see this later when we discuss the *xueqi.* We know that the difference in the quality between meridians is expressed in several chapters in the Nei jing in terms of variation of the composition of *xue* and *qi.* At the level of *xueqi* we have variations and fluctuations, but that does not occur as such at the level of *jingshen* or *jingqi.*

QI 氣

Elisabeth Rochat: The first thing that we see in the character for *qi* is that there is the same bursting grain of cereal or rice as in *jing* (米). But what is added is not the colour of the inner vitality in action, but just the image of an exhalation (气). It is this movement of animation which is the result of transformation. It is not a substance or a visible sign of activity, but just an exhalation and a releasing of something. That is *qi*. But of course there is no emanation if it is not coming from something. This character *qi* is very difficult to understand and translate because it has several degrees of meaning, always according to context.

At the first level it is all that exists, because all things exist by virtue of a movement, and by the continuation of this movement. Also, all the effects of the transformation are due to *qi* and in a way this *qi* is all the relationships, influences, ways of receiving and adapting those influences, and all things, and living beings. For instance, there is a very famous statement in Ling shu chapter 30:

'Huangdi: I know that a human possesses *jing, qi, jin, ye, xue* and *mai*. At the deepest understanding they are all one *qi,* but they are differentiated by six names. I want to know what the meaning of each of them is.'

Then there comes the definition of each of the six. At the end of the chapter this is repeated and it is said that *qi* can be one of the six *qi.* This is not surprising in classical Chinese texts. The meaning is that this is all one *qi* or one unique *qi,* and it is the unity of life. But within this unity of life we have to differentiate how the couples organize themselves. We also have to consider the movement of life and all the substance through which this animation can express and develop itself, such as blood or essences. We can see that in this example the liquids are two of the six *qi* composing the unique *qi.* If you call *qi* all that exists, when you are in a context where you have *qi* in a dual expression with one of these things, for example in the couple *jingqi,* the *qi* is not all that exists. This *qi* is the complement to the essences in order to make life in the innermost part.

With numerology you can just add one number and the meaning of *qi* changes. For instance with one, *yi qi* (一 氣), generally speaking this is the great *qi* which fills the void between heaven and earth. It is a void only because it has free circulation of all this *qi*. This is also the great unity of life because all living beings, all these particular notes of life, are in a way related and supported by this great source of life which is also the model of all life. This is the great movement between heaven and earth. This is nothing other than the original *qi*, and it is called the original *qi* not only in medical books but in a lot of other texts. This original *qi* is the specification of the source of life in a particular form. It is particularly inscribed in a special structure in the composition of the essences with a special nature and a kind of destiny, and it is something which we share with all other beings because it is just a particularization of this great movement of life. It is an emergence, a temporary or casual emergence of that original *qi*. All that is an expression of the one *qi*. If I am just looking at this great mass of the 10,000 beings, I see it like that. I consider myself as this particular expression of original *qi*, and want to use it in a good way in the manner of this great model of life, which is the best way to preserve it or prevent decline. This is the same thing as good health. You do not use your essences or forces, you just let the spirits ride life.

If you have two *qi* (*er qi* 二 氣), or *qi* at the level of two, the meaning is *yinyang*.

Three *qi* (*san qi* 三 氣) are generally the three constitutive components of the universe, with clear heaven, unclear earth and the mixing in the median as man. But it is also all the threefold expression of animation. For instance it is the triple heater, which in the Nan jing is called the agent for the differentiation and distribution of the original *qi*. It is also the organization of the unity of life in three great functions, the ancestral *qi*, the nutritive *qi* and the defensive *qi*. Always this expression of three has the same origin because these three *qi* have the same origin. They draw their deep quality from the original *qi* and from the original forces of man and they have a specificity due to their use and the place in which they are located for their distribution.

For instance the *zong qi* (宗 氣), the ancestral *qi*, being above the diaphragm is the conjunction of the purest essences which make the beating of the correct and pure *qi* and are able to order and follow the good rhythm of all the distribution of the *qi* throughout the body. *Zong* is like an ancestor, a chief who gathers under his roof all which belongs to his family of *qi* inside the body. The nutritive *qi* (*ying qi* 營 氣) attaches to the middle heater and to the essences coming from the spleen and stomach. It has the ability to distribute and to put in the right place all the elements for rebuilding and maintenance inside the body. In a medical book three *qi* usually refers to these three qualities of *qi*, but here it is the more general meaning of three, which is the three great components of life in the universe. In specialist books you can have three *qi* with particular meanings dependent on the category of science the book is dealing with.

Si qi (四 氣), *qi* at the level of four or four *qi*, are the four seasons, or the specific influences coming from the four seasons. Here we have the very important element of the unfolding of time, because if we have *qi* as the components of form in the body, *qi* is also a component of time. There is a reality of time. Time is not an abstract concept, time is the succession of moments, each of which has a particular quality and a particular influence on the great movement of the universe and all the movement inside an organism. All the push or restraint to the circulation and all the variation inside the transformation are due to the particular quality of the moment. It is a moment of the day but a moment of the year as well, and the four seasons are the model for this variation of the influence coming from the environment. We find this particularly with *xueqi* because it is very important in the maintenance of the balance of the *xueqi* to be able to adapt instantly.

The *wu qi* (五 氣), the five *qi*, are the five elements or the five *zang* or the specific *qi* of the five *zang*. Or they are the five atmospheric influences coming from heaven to earth, or a mixture of all these influences resulting in all kinds of variation such as tornadoes or violent rains. All that is in exactly the same image of the model of the movement in the five *zang* or the five emotions or the five wills. Of course we can have fear or anger but not for too long, and it is always best to come back to a balance because this is what happens between heaven and earth for the maintenance of life.

The *liu qi* (六 氣), the six *qi*, are the six atmospheric influences. These are not the same as the five but are like principles coming from heaven to nourish or attack man. They are also the six principles of the vital maintenance in a human body. Six is for maintenance. Five was for the emanation of life from the innermost place.

The periods of the solar calendar in Chinese are called the 24 *qi* (*qi jie* 氣 節). You can see that *qi* is everything which gives the continuity and the passage of movement in time or in space, covering all aspects of life. The names of these periods such as Little Snow or Big White Cold, are given because they express the reality of the influence seen in life on earth. It is the visibility of time.

At the level of two, one *qi* is no longer all that exists; it is already *yinyang*. Even if we are talking of *yang qi*, or *yin qi* there is always a composition. There is no pure *yang qi* inside the body although we talk of *yang qi*. It is the surging of life, the animation and all the force of life. We can see this in Ling shu chapter 8:

'Heaven in me is virtue. Earth in me is *qi*. Virtue flows, *qi* spreads out and there is life.'

After that we have all the particular names for the varieties of animation, for instance the *qi* of the liver or the defensive *qi* (*wei qi* 衛 氣), or the *qi* of a particular meridian. This is just to be able to analyse and speak of a specific aspect of life.

What we can say is that the *qi* which is at the level of indivisible *qi*, is useful because from that we have the unity in the origin, the community of all living beings, and also the unity of myself and the unfolding of my life. There is something which is seen in different ways, different expressions and different variations, for instance defensive *qi* or ancestral *qi*, but there is always something in common which is enough to support them in the same activity.

Pathology is always found at the level of different names and functions, and we have to detect the dysfunction and rebalance each couple at each level. In the human body where does the *qi* come from? For example with essences there is original *qi* and the *qi* coming from posterior heaven or the assimilation of elements from the surroundings and the environment. The original *qi* is linked to the kidneys and sometimes to *ming men*, with the *qi* expressing a movement for the regulation of life in the rhythmic beating between the two kidneys. This is mentioned in the Nan jing, particularly in difficulties 8 and 66, where there is quite a good description. There is a kind of secret beating between the two kidneys, like the pull of this primitive animation, which allows the water and the *yin* to express the fire of life which is working deeply inside the *yin*. This normal manifestation of life could not happen without a structure, inside a body, with something to balance the *qi* in order to maintain the regularity and to keep the movement going on. Another thing is that the secret aspect of this corresponds to the beating of the heart, which is the manifestation of the same movement of life. The beating of the heart also depends on the ancestral *qi.* The ancestral *qi* is nothing other than the conjunction of all the *qi* of the body, filtered by the diaphragm, and animated by the connection with this root of all the movement inside the body which is the original *qi, yuan qi* (原 氣).

Yuan (原) is the image of a source, with a rock on the left, and water flowing from a source in this rock. The water is white, clear and pure. This is pure water flowing from a source in a rocky mountain. The image of this original *qi* is like the undying, constant source of what gives the first spring to a current of water. After that we have rain and water coming from other rivulets and so on, but at the very beginning the strength of the river starts at the source. It continues to become a stream and a river but if the source dries up something is clearly wrong.

Another way to write *yuan* is like this: 元. It is the same pronunciation, but this character's meaning is the principle of the origin, it is more mysterious in a way. In the first character we had something which appears and is flowing silently and quite impulsively, but continuously. Here we have the mysterious side of this source. This is the original *qi* which makes the real continuity of life.

There are all the other kinds of *qi* which come from the transformation of food in particular. But original *qi* is always present. It supports the effort and the quality of the *qi* everywhere within the body. For instance, as far as the *zang* are concerned they are supported in their activity by the fire of *ming men* (命 門) and of the kidneys or original *qi*, and their activity supports the essences in the continual renewal of their releasing. It is always a kind of cycle and its effects are clearly visible. The kidneys govern the original *qi*, the spleen and stomach govern the renewal of *qi* from alimentation, and the lungs govern the absorption of *qi* from respiration. This is the way to fill oneself with the quality of the surrounding environment as it is at that precise moment. This is the reason why the lungs are so important in the mastery of the *qi*, but are also very fragile. They are called the fragile *zang* because they are exposed to the direct penetration of influences coming from the exterior. The lungs master the *qi* and the sea of *qi* in the middle of the chest, *tan zhong* (膻 中). All these expressions have nearly the same function, to order a good distribution of *qi* throughout the body.

What is interesting is that the three female *zang*, the kidneys, spleen and lungs are very important for the production of *qi*, and we will see the contrary with blood, The female *zang* are also in charge, in another way, of all the transformation of water and liquids in the body. I do not say that the liver and heart are of no importance for the *qi*, but they are not directly implied in the renewal and original emanation of it, even if they are active in creating its movement inside the body. The liver gives strength to all the circulation, and the heart gives the impulse to all the circulation throughout the network of animation, particularly the circulation of blood.

FUNCTIONS OF QI
ANIMATING

Elisabeth Rochat: This function is the role of animating and setting in motion. This is not only for the various kinds of circulation in an adult, but also the strength leading to the development of the embryo into the child, and from the child to the adult. This process is also due to the vitality of the *qi*, not just the original *qi* (*yuan qi* 原 氣), but all the expressions of *qi* and the real continuity of life through the *yuan qi* with the cooperation of all the other kinds of *qi* and essences. For instance, insufficiency of *qi* could lead to a slowing down in the growth process, a general weakness in the functioning of the *zangfu* or the circulation through meridians and the network of animation, or a weakness in the circulation and distribution of blood and bodily liquids, and all kinds of other elements including nutrition.

WARMING

The second function of the *qi* is warming. This is the regulation of the bodily temperature. We call this the warming action of the *qi*, but it is always the continuity of this process which we can see. For instance, if there is a blockage there is no circulation and circulation is part of the movement to maintain the temperature. Transportation at a subtle level is warmth. For instance liquids are transported not as a mass but as a vapour, and the transportation of liquids from place to place and the activity of this transformation includes the maintenance of the right temperature. This is described very well in Ling shu chapter 30. It is a description of what is called *qi*, as one of the six *qi*.

'The upper heater spreads and propagates the taste of the five grains. It invades the skin like smoke.'

This is exactly the image of this vapour at the right temperature.

'It gives power and strength to the body and moisture to the body hair. It is like mist (*wu* 霧) and dew (*lu* 露).

This is the double aspect.

'That is called *qi*.'

In definitions of *qi* we always have these double sides. It is not just the power of animation or circulation, it is also the ability to maintain what is circulating at a good level of warmth. This is the reality of defence for instance. Because if all that is going well, we have the third function of *qi* as a result.

PROTECTING

There is protection or defence if the layers of the skin are well irrigated with vapours, the right temperature is maintained, there is no problem in the good rhythm of opening and closing of the pores, and no problem in following the natural rhythm of life, day and night, winter and summer. If this is the case there will always be the means to resist invasion by perverse influences. If the circulation is good then if there is some cold which comes treacherously near, you can feel it because there is a free circulation between this place and the depths of your heart and spirits. There is a kind of signal and you arc able to react and make a defence, or increase the temperature and increase the functions of vapourization and liquids with warmth at that place to push away the perverse force.

This is very well described in Ling shu chapter 27. This is what is called protection against the perverse, and the defensive role of the *qi*. If the signal is not perceived and the reaction started at that very superficial level then it must be felt at a deeper level. If this is so or if I am really unable to perceive and to react to this signal at all, then I have to go and see my acupuncturist!

FIRMNESS IN HOLDING

A stream is a stream because there is a current as well as the water itself. The water of a stream does not flow everywhere, it is the strength of the current in the stream which makes the stream. The character for water (*shui* 水) shows that something is flowing very carefully within the three strokes. The trigram *kan*, which is related to the virtue of water, shows the same thing, with the strong *yang* line within the two weak *yin* lines. We have this same kind of *yang* movement maintaining the flow of liquids.

I think this is something very deep and very ancient in Chinese thought, and there are several applications of it. One is the circulation of blood. For instance, what is the definition of the *mai* (脈)? Ling shu chapter 30 gives a description of it as the network for animation, but sometimes it is translated as vessel. It is also the pulse. We will look at the meaning of the pulse when we study *xueqi*. What is a vessel? It is just the pipe or the conduit for this blood. But it is only the perceptible form or shape, the manifestation of what is maintaining the blood in good circulation. It is the current inside the blood which is primarily giving the direction of the circulation and maintaining the circulation. We know this because if there is some kind of weakness of the *qi* or overheating of the blood we can have a haemorrhage. So it is not only the vessels which are able to maintain the circulation of blood, and the vessels are not only veins or arteries but also the smallest capillaries.

The description of the *mai* in the Ling shu compares it to dykes and banks maintaining the nutritive *qi* in a good circulation, preventing it from escaping or being led astray in a wrong direction. This is one of the aspects of the efficiency of the *qi*, to be able to maintain the blood or to maintain all kinds of liquids in a good distribution, in the form of vapour, dew and smoke and so on. But also according to this ability of the *qi* to give a good rhythm of opening and closing, it is able to maintain liquids inside the body or to make evacuations outside at the right time, in the form of urine or sweat for example. The functioning of the *qi* is always involved in the regulation of the centre, and in all the opening and closing of the doors of the body. It is also in charge of the good maintenance and the holding or guarding of the special essences, for instance of the sperm. You can have spermatorrhea due to weakness of the *qi*, or for a woman there can be vaginal discharge.

TRANSFORMING

Hua (化) is transformation. The activity of transformation achieved by the *qi* of the lower heater allows the reabsorption of certain parts of the liquids and the elimination of others. It is exactly like the great movement between heaven and earth. When the liquids arrive at the lower heater, the *qi* by its animation and warmth causes a rising up of vapours. What is rising up is obviously the most subtle and purest element which is full of essential vitality. What remains is just more dense, heavier, and it becomes urine and is evacuated in order to allow the continuation of the transformation. If there is no evacuation there is no longer good transformation or the right level of temperature and activity because the *qi* cannot cope with the situation. You can have inflammation and swelling, or weakness of the *qi* because the liquids overwhelm the strength of the *qi*. As a result you have weakness of the defence as well as a swelling in the belly or in the tissues.

Transformation due to the *qi* is always very important in the middle heater because transformation is nothing other than digestion and assimilation. It is essential for the renewal of life. Throughout the body and the general activity of what is called the triple heater we also have the effect of this transformation of *qi* maintaining a good balance between elements such as liquids or nutrition, and the power which is able to make them circulate as incorporated elements. All that is the effect of transformation, and transformation is due to the quality of the *qi.* All the regulation of the *zang* through the meridians and the *luo* and so on are dependent on the *qi* and its quality.

The five *zang* are continuously transforming the essences in order to maintain life. This transformation occurs thanks to the *qi* which is already in the body, and the result of the transformation is the releasing of *qi,* in both physiolgical and psychological aspects. We need *qi* to transform and we need transformation to produce *qi.* This interplay and transformation of essences is the vital operation of life.

When the *qi* is functioning well, there is good rhythm in all the circulation, in all the functions of opening and closing (for example the opening and closing of the pores of the skin) and all regulation of the rhythm of life, according to night and day, activity and rest.

TYPES OF QI
ZONG QI 宗 氣

Elisabeth Rochat: References to this are found in Ling shu chapters 71 and 75, and Su wen 18. In Ling shu 71 it says:

'The five grains enter the stomach. They are divided in three ways: the waste, the *jinye* and the ancestral *qi*. The *zong qi*, the ancestral *qi*, accumulates in the middle of the chest and goes out at the larynx through the *mai* of the heart to activate exhalation and inhalation.'

This means that all the purest essences making the best of the *qi* are just collected up here in this very special and high powered area above the diaphragm in the chest. Because of their purity and their high power they are able to give a good rhythm to the whole circulation of *qi*. One example of this is respiration. The rhythm of respiration is part of natural life and is part of the way by which the lungs are able to give a good rhythm to the whole circulation in the meridians and to 'receive the 100 *mai* at the morning audience'.

In Su wen chapter 18 it says that *zong qi* is formed by the conjunction of what is coming from the middle heater and the air from the lungs. It gives a rhythm to the beating of the heart, which is another way to give a general rhythm or circulation throughout the body. The relationship between respiration and the beating of the heart must be good, and this is also very significant when you are taking pulses because they give an indication of the state of the balance between what must be the unique rhythm of life. This is the reason why *zong qi* is really nothing other than this kind of commanding pulse for all the distribution inside the body, the distribution of all kinds of elements due to the strength and animation given by the *qi*. *Zong qi* does not circulate itself but just gives the rhythm, like a sea.

The sea in itself is an inexhaustible reservoir. We have had the image of a source, but on the other hand we have the image of the sea which is able to receive the 100 rivers without overflowing. The sea is also able to endure seasons of dryness without experiencing a diminution of its level. The sea attracts all the rivers and gives to all the clouds. In the *zong qi* we have the sea of *qi* in the middle of the chest. It attracts all kinds of *qi* coming from the organism without ever overflowing. In fact the lungs, as the master of the *qi*, are the unity of the *qi* of the organism. In another way the sea has the role of ensuring distribution, as in making clouds. This is like the image of the fog and dew coming to irrigate all the body from the upper heater, as given in Ling shu chapter 30. Because this is a sea it is not affected by the flow of one particular river or by an excess or insufficiency of another one. It is able to regulate the *qi* totally and consistently. This is also true for all the seas within the body according to which systems they affect.

The character for *zong* is a temple for sacrifice to the ancestors, an ancestral hall (宗) (cf Wieger Lesson 36). The upper part is the building and below there is an emanation, perhaps from the sacrifice. It is an influx coming from heaven. Perhaps it comes in answer to the sacrifice? You then have to interpret this answer as auspicious or not. It is through the worship of ancestors that you nourish and maintain life after their death, and you cannot do this with very solid things because the ancestors are in a very subtle kind of life. They cannot be nourished by something having a form like a grain. But they can be comforted and given strength by emanations coming from alcohol or the burning of meat or from music played on these special occasions, or from the emanations coming from the feelings excited in all the people belonging to the same lineage. All that brings to the ancestor some kind of essence which make his life in the higher state longer in a mysterious way. That is the reason why it is very important to have children to continue the worship, because it is your own life after your death which is at stake.

In ancient times, certainly, it was also believed that because ancestors were in heaven they had very real power over the living decendents, and these rituals were also a way of protecting themselves against the bad feelings of the dead ancestors. If you fulfilled all the rites correctly then you could gain the benefits. Little by little through the centuries this fear of ancestors slowly became the need of the ancestors. By the Han dynasty there was not such fear but there was the idea that the ancestors really needed the living for their survival. All kinds of superstitions remained through the centuries, but things slowly changed between the Shang dynasty of the 12th century BC or as far back as we can know, and the Han dynasty of around 200 BC-200 AD.

The lower part of this character zong (示) is the same as on the left side of shen (神). It is linked with the idea that the shen come from above, and that they are behind all dual expressions of vitality. Normally zong qi is an expression of posterior heaven. We can contrast it with the character zu (祖) which also means ancestor but which is not the same. The translation of zu is 'founder'.

On the left of the character is the same element (示) as is found underneath in the character zong (宗), and on the right is the part representing the power of the founder, for instance the first ancestor (且). Zu appears very often in the posthumous name of the founder of an imperial dynasty. But it never appears in the names of other emperors of the same dynasty. There is only one founder, and only the originator of the lineage has this kind of power which is able to extend and continue itself throughout the dynasty.

When you have zong you do not have the image of the origin, it is never used in Chinese literature in this way, that is always zu. Normally, according to 'The Book of Rites' at the time of the Han dynasty, if you were a prince or a high class person when you worshipped an ancestor you worshipped him in a special temple, and in the temple you had tablets representing the power of the ancestors set out in special positions. The tablet of the founder, the tai zu (太祖), always remained in one commanding position at the western end of the formation. When someone died the other tablets moved up one place, father to grandfather, grandfather to great grandfather, with the most recent death becoming the father.

The meaning of ancestral, *zong*, is very close to all this, because an ancestor is not only the great honoured father, but the father who gathers under his authority all the members of the family. This type of *zong* is not only an ancestor but also the chief of the cult of the worship of ancestors. He is the man who gathers together the worshipers, and makes a unity of all the members of the same family who come to worship the ancestor. We have here the idea of giving homage to those who were here before and from whom we are descended.

At the same time in posterior heaven we have the need to follow the continuance of life, and to maintain the family in good rule and attract favourable effects through this worship. All these things are involved in worship of ancestors. And this is the meaning of *zong*. It is the faithfulness to the founder. It is the continuity of life through its various elements and successions of time progressively revealing the power which was in the first ancestor. The first ancestor is analogous to original *qi*.

YING QI 營 氣

Normally *ying* is translated as nutritive. We have the double image of fire (火) on top of the character. It is for the expansion of the movement, and some kind of warmth; a gentle warmth of life. In the lower part there is the image of a primitive settlement (宮) with a ground plan of two tents or huts inside a fence. So first of all the character has the meaning of an established plan and the building of something in accordance with that. For example, it might mean to establish a military camp. 'Nutritive' is a good expression but it is not exactly the full meaning of the character which is really to rebuild or reconstruct. If you establish a camp for soldiers to rest and to be nourished in before sleep, you also have to defend them. There is no defence without building, and no building without defence. It is the same as the image in the Bible where you have a sword in one hand and a ploughshare in the other. If you are not able to defend territory you cannot build or maintain anything, but if you are not able to maintain something you have no real defence. This is a reality which we have known for hundreds and hundreds of years.

WEI QI 衛 氣

There are two parts to the character wei (衛). On the outside is *xing* (行), which is circulation, conduct, a kind of well balanced marching. It means to walk and to act regularly and correctly, and is all kinds of regulated conduct of life, activity or morality. It is also the character for element as in five elements, because they are the five agents of regulation and five powers of giving and maintaining life, the way to conduct life regularly.

Inside this character *xing* you have the image of leather (韋). There are two kinds of leather: with or without preparation. This one is leather which has been prepared. The traditional etymology shows two men pulling the same object in opposite directions. It is probably referring to tanning leather in some way (cf Wieger Lesson 31G). The raw leather was used to make shields. But this is also the image of a guard on the high wall of a palace or castle, ensuring its defence. Part of defence is to see what is coming and not to have too many distractions. Defence is made with a kind of circulation and a regulation of movement.

ZHEN QI 真 氣

This is authentic *qi*. The character has the number ten (十) at the top immediately above an eye (目). So you have ten eyes looking at something and not finding anything wrong. Everything is perfect. This is the etymology. The meaning is that what is authentic is such that there is no diversion from the current or direction given at the origin. All is following the natural pattern of life in the special expression which is myself. I am just fulfilling my destiny.

Fulfilling your destiny is just guiding your life with essences, spirits and *qi* according to the great rule of cosmic animation as expressed in yourself. You can react precisely because the firmness and stability of the interior is perfectly in tune with all the stimulation and influences coming from the exterior, constantly adapting oneself to circumstances, small and large. If all is like that nothing is wrong, and everything is circulating well. Liquids are always and everywhere transformed in order to be incorporated and useful, blood circulates well and regularly, and you are saving and sparing your essences for the benefit of your inner vision.

And because your inner vision and life are strong you are not expending your essences in too much movement in relation to the exterior. The axis of life is firm and well oriented, and all the distribution of *qi* is well made. All kinds of excitation and passion soon recover their balance. This is called authentic, and it is also called authentic *qi*. Authentic *qi* is the *qi* of my life when it is expressing my original pattern, my true nature.

ZHENG QI 正 氣

Zheng qi is not exactly authentic, it is regular. Regular, normal, without diversion, following the right way. Normally a meridian is *zheng*, because it is the norm for circulation. What is called *zheng qi* is all kinds of *qi* and animation following the norms of life regularly without diversion and perversion - making everything correct, following the norm.

This is exactly the contrary of perverse *qi*, *xie qi* (邪 氣). Perverse is what is not straight, what is oblique. With *zheng qi* you are correct because you are straight. *Zheng qi* is all *qi* which is not perverse, and if the *qi* is not *zheng* it is perverse. It must be one or the other. *Yuan qi* is never perverse, because it is just the continuity of the springing up of my life. *Ying qi* and *wei qi* are never perverse either. They can be in bad relationships or weak, thus allowing the perverse to invade the person, but in themselves they are just defending or building. If the defence is not defending it is no longer the defence.

It is the same thing with bodily liquids, when they leave the body they are no longer bodily liquids, and their name changes from *jinye* to saliva or urine or sweat. Perversion is just a change in the nature of something.

ZHONG QI 中 氣

Zhong qi is an expression in Chinese medical and classical texts meaning central *qi* or *qi* of the middle heater. This is one of the most frequent uses of this expression. In modern books it is only used as the *qi* of the middle heater, or spleen and stomach. Sometimes it was used to mean *qi* of the centre, but we do not know what the centre is. If the centre is the middle it could could be all five *zang* or it could be something else. But that is a very particular use, and not very common. *Zhong* can be the centre or the median, something like the median void. I prefer this to the translation of 'middle', because *zhong* is a centre in the manner of an intermediary. A centre is always a place of exchange.

DA QI 大 氣

Da qi, great *qi*, is the name of the *qi* of the environment, or the *qi* of respiration. This is the same thing as the *qi* of nature which we can assimilate by respiration. For instance in the Ling shu it says that *da qi* is given by heaven. It is celestial influences touching the earth and penetrating man by the way of the lungs. Sometimes by assimilation it can be the name of the *qi* of the sea of *qi* in the middle of the chest. *Da* can also mean powerful.

Question: Is this the *qi* that you can absorb through the pores of the skin?

Elisabeth Rochat: Normally if this *da qi* is all the surrounding *qi* you can be in contact with the *da qi* via your skin, but generally texts do not emphasize this aspect.

XUE 血 BLOOD

Elisabeth Rochat: The character *xue* (血) is a vessel with something treasured inside, which is the blood. Blood circulates through vessels called the *mai* (脈), the network of animation. The *mai* is a kind of force to carry and contain the current which is animating the blood. It is like the banks of a river. But the *mai* is quite inseparable from the blood, and for instance in Su wen chapter 17 it is called the *fu* (府), the palace or depot, for the blood.

Blood is under the mastery of the heart. There is in fact no blood inside the body which has not passed through the heart. This is the main difference between blood and all the other bodily liquids. The red colour is given from the depths of the heart to this liquid which then makes the blood and which is one expression of the mystery of life.

Ling shu chapter 18 says:

'The middle heater is also associated with the middle of the stomach… The *qi* received by the middle heater filters the residues and waste, vapourizes the bodily liquids, transforms the *jing wei*, rises and spreads in the *mai* of the lungs, and finally there is transformation and it becomes blood bringing life to the body. Nothing is more precious.'

Another text in Ling shu chapter 81 says:

'The middle heater makes the *qi* come out like a dew, and it rises up powerfully, to spread inside the great and small valleys. It pervades all the network of animation even the smallest. When all the bodily liquids are in total, perfect harmonious composition there is change and transformation; it becomes red and thus this is blood.'

This is one way of saying that there is a common origin for the blood and for all kinds of bodily liquids in the spleen. Normally some of these liquids which are very rich and dense with essences rise up through the diaphragm because essences are able to pass through very fine filters. These liquids enter the lungs and absorb oxygen, or the *qi* coming from respiration, but it is only because they pass through the heart that they become rcd. Red is the colour of life, the colour of fire, the colour of the heart, and the mark or sign of the heart on these special liquids. We will see that it is more important than a simple change of colour because this mark of the heart is also the mark of the spirits.

So what is the difference between the blood and the nutritive power, the *ying qi?* It is that in the blood there is not only this nutritive power, but also a kind of offering of life. This offering of life, as is said in chapter 18 of Ling shu, is the regularity of animation because the beating of the heart is regular and the pulsation in the network of animation must also be regular. The presence of the blood throughout the body has the same regularity day and night, winter and summer. This kind of regularity in the circulation of blood depends on the heart.

In addition to this, through the presence of the heart and the spirit of the heart in the blood there is also an ability to perceive. This perception is located in the blood because we are able to perceive by virtue of the presence of the spirits and through the depths of one's consciousness. The heart is the dwelling place of the spirits, and if the blood is more loaded than other liquids with the presence of the spirits or by the attraction and effect of the spirits, it is through the blood and the good circulation of blood that all kinds of sensation and perception can occur.

Of course through defence and nutrition we also have the effect of mixing with the blood and the presence of spirits because spirits are also absolutely everywhere. But the blood is always a very specific vector of information, and in a way part of the function of our nervous system is controlled by blood which is animated by the *qi,* and circulates through the network of animation in this correspondence with the heart. This is why it is said that the blood is under the mastery of the heart.

Through all this we know the importance of the blood in the movements of the psyche. We know, for instance, that emptiness of blood or heat in the blood causes a weakness or a disorder in the relationship with the spirits, which can easily lead to mental disturbance or madness. This is because the spirits have to rely on the blood to express themselves everywhere. It is not exactly the same thing as with the *jingshen*. It is more precise here, with the specific materialization of the blood and the regular circulation.

RELATIONSHIP WITH THE LIVER

The liver is in charge of storing the blood. But to be able to store is also to be able to free at the right time. The liver is the keeper of the blood because it is in charge of liberating and spreading blood when it is needed, for instance when the regular circulation given by the heart is not enough for the circumstances, or in a specific location. For example, in an intense muscular effort you need an increased amount of blood. This is not coming from the heart but from the liver. It is mixed with the function of the liver to master the muscular forces.

There is also another irregularity which is that between day and night. For instance, in the night, as is said in Su wen chapter 10, blood returns to the liver because we do not need to expend blood or essences with all the effort for communication or movement and so on. But we need this blood returned to the liver to nourish the *hun* (魂) and to be impregnated by them and to allow real dreams. At the same time the defensive *qi* is also returning to the inside during the night. All the stabilization is done during the night, during this time of rest. So the liver is very important too for all kinds of irregular utilization of the blood, and with this alternation of being turned to the exterior during the day and turned to the nourishment of the interior during the night. This acts in synergy with the defensive *qi* which works in the interior during the night.

RELATIONSHIP WITH THE SPLEEN

The spleen commands or manages the blood. This is not in the same way as the heart does, but with the notion of gathering. The Chinese for this function is *pi tong xue* (脾 統 血). To manage is to hold. To hold is to hold together and gather. How can the spleen do that with blood? The spleen gives its form to the blood by the production of the bodily liquids and the juices which are the raw material for the making of the blood. Therefore the liquid form of the blood is given by the work of the spleen. Another thing is that the quality and the density and the richness of the juices determine the density and quality of the blood, which is then more or less able to be animated by the *qi* and to remain inside the *mai*. If the essences are lacking and the liquids do not have so many essences, then the real quality of the blood is not so good and it can easily leave the conduits of circulation. That would depend on the *qi* but also it depends on the special density of the blood. Because of all that we can say that the spleen manages the blood.

The character for *tong* (統) is made with the thread of silk on the left side, which represents all kinds of networks and links. On the right the character means powerful, or a strong power. It is the fullness of power. So *tong* is to be able to hold and to maintain in a network what makes the power. *Tong* is also used to mean chairman too. But with the spleen it is linked to the ability to offer juices of rich quality which will make the blood. Once it is blood it is under the control of the spleen to remain a rich liquid.

There is a solidarity between the blood and the bodily fluids. There is a very good passage in chapter 71 of Ling shu:

'The *ying qi* makes the bodily liquids by secretion. They spread into the *mai* and make blood through transformation.'

Here part of the nutritive *qi* is taken to be impregnated by the *qi* of the lungs and through the activity of the heart becomes red, and that is the blood. So what is the difference between the nutritive *qi* and the *jinye* and so on? It is in the function. The *ying qi* is the origin of all kinds of distribution and reconstruction of the liquids, and whether the bodily liquids and blood are rich and renewed depends on the quality of the transformation of the spleen. The spleen is in charge of giving the blood shape and form. It is the movement of the earth element.

It is strange to find a kind of bonding of the heart and the liver in the case of the blood. The heart masters blood and the liver stores it, and these two *zang* correspond to the most *yang* movements of the five elements which are in charge of the blood. Of course we saw that the spleen is at the origin of all kinds of renewal of the blood as well as of the *qi.* And how can the blood circulate if it is not through the *qi,* especially at the level of the upper heater which partly depends on the power of the lung? This is also the second link between the blood and the lungs. The first link was the penetration or impregnation by the *qi* of respiration. With the distribution, even if it is through the beating and the movement of the heart, this movement is relying on the *qi* of the sea of *qi,* and all that is an aspect of functioning.

RELATIONSHIP WITH THE KIDNEYS

As far as the kidneys are concerned I think their relationship with blood is another kind of relationship with the essences. There is a kind of power in the essences, given by the kidneys, which is also present in the blood. In some texts and classical commentaries we have the idea of the essential power of the blood linked with the power of the kidneys. Do not forget that the *yin* of the kidneys is just said to generate the liver, and the liver is the keeper and storer of the blood. If the kidneys are giving their *yin* side to the liver, and if the *yin* of the liver is nothing other than the blood of the liver, then we have a very strong link here between the blood and the essences of the kidneys. This is very well described in some classical commentaries, for example some texts of the 6th and 7th centuries AD. You can find this in modern books too, and sometimes I wonder if they are not influenced by occidental medicine and the role of the marrow in haematopoiesis (the making of the blood).

XUE QI 血 氣 BLOOD AND QI

Elisabeth Rochat: Now we will look at the special relationship between blood and *qi,* and after that we will look in the Nei jing itself in order to see how the couple *xueqi* (血 氣) is something different and more powerful than the simple relationship between one liquid called blood and one force called *qi.*

This relationship between blood and *qi* is one of the most total intimacy. In a way they have the same origin because the renewal of both of them comes from the transformation of liquids and grains through the stomach and spleen, and they both rely on the power of the origin to remain faithful to their own natures. But nevertheless although they have the same origin they express this power of life in two different ways. *Qi* does not have any kind of form. It is dependent on the *yang,* and it is for giving animation and setting in motion. On the other hand blood always has a kind of shape, even if it is a shape in the likeness of water and is dependent on the *yin.* It is mostly in charge of nourishing and the maintenance of life by humidification, irrigation and so on. For this reason blood and *qi* can mix together to make an inseparable composition. In this composition one helps the other. For example, *qi* is very useful in the production of the blood because without the transformation due to the *qi* there is no possibility of transforming food in order to make the rich juice giving the form of the basic substance for the production of blood. We can see that in pathology an emptiness of *qi* can lead little by little to an emptiness of blood due to this lack of transformation and production of the basic substance of blood.

The other relationship is that *qi* is able to make the blood circulate efficiently. There are a lot of sentences in medical texts such as 'When the *qi* is circulating well, blood is also circulating well.' The impulse upon which the circulation of blood depends comes from this power of the upper heater expressed by the lung and heart and gathered in the sea of *qi* in the middle of the chest. Through that we see this circulation of blood not only in the meridians but in any kind of circulation in any *mai,* from the greatest meridians and vessels to the most subtle and smallest capillaries. We also see that the *qi* holds the blood in this circulation and guides the blood.

On the other hand, it is also said in Chinese classical commentaries that the blood is the mother of the *qi.* There is no *yang* if it does not come from the effect of releasing some kind of essences from a *yin* substance. Blood is the special shape taken by essences in order to allow the releasing of some kind of energy and *yang* effect. If there is not enough to stabilize the *qi*, this power just exhausts and dissipates itself uselessly outside. This is what is called in other circumstances the *yang* without root. There are signs of this such as a superficial pulse without a root. It is very dangerous because it is a sign of a deep dissociation between *yin* and *yang*. This is one of the main functions of the *yin* essences and liquids, to attract and fix the extent of the *qi* and by that to make it useful and working. *Qi* without blood is unable to do anything. There would be no circulation and no transformation and no real impulse or warming were it not for the action of the *qi* within the *yin* support. This is expressed in the couple *xueqi.*

Of course we know that it is not only the blood, it is the same with the *jinye*. When you have night sweats when you are sleeping they may be due to an emptiness of *yin*. This is due to the emptiness of the kidneys. The *yang* is without effect if it is not in an harmonious composition with a good quality and quantity of *yin*. This is also one of the reasons why blood is called the mother of the *qi*.

Through this we can see that the couple *xueqi* also has several levels of interpretation. The first is just what you could call the circulation of blood. But in fact very often in classical texts what is called *xueqi* is much more than that, it is behind this blood in circulation and is the representation of the total composition of *yinyang* in the body. The blood is linked with all the other liquids in the body and the *qi* which animates the blood is also just an expression of the *qi* of the body. This is the why the couple also has the very general meaning of the complete balance, interplay and interpenetration of the *yin* and *yang* of all kinds of liquids coming from the essences, and of the *qi*. They join their qualities to make something efficient for life. This is certainly the reason why *xueqi* as a couple is so important in the presentation of Chinese physiology and pathology. Of course the pathology has symptoms of *qi* and symptoms of blood, but generally they are seen together.

BLOOD AND QI IN THE NEI JING
COSMIC CORRESPONDENCE

Elisabeth Rochat: Firstly we will look at cosmic correspondence. By this we mean the way to describe *xueqi* in a human being made with blood and flesh if we are looking at nature or heaven and earth. This is very interesting. After that we will consider *xueqi* in relationship with the origin and the renewal of anterior and posterior heaven. Also we will point out the difference of level between what we call blood and what we call essences. In a way the blood is these essences, but it is not exactly the same thing.

Then we will see this couple *xueqi* not only in the rebuilding of the body but also in the expression of the spirit. We will see the difference between the couples *jingshen* and *xueqi*. Then we will consider *xueqi* as the best example of the harmony between *yin* and *yang* in the body, which is the reason why it is also through the perception of *xueqi* that diagnosis is possible. Finally we have to consider that the normality of *xueqi* is in its variation and fluctuation. Somewhere we also have the idea that in this variation is the fundamental and structural difference of the composition in the blood and *qi* for each of the twelve meridians.

SU WEN CHAPTER 20

First let us see what I call the cosmic correspondence. In Su wen chapter 20 the Emperor asks the question:

'I wish to know completely the natural laws (the supreme numbers, *zhi shu* 至 數) of heaven and earth which are a unity (*he* 合) with the blood and *qi* of the human body, and through which one has the understanding to give the correct diagnosis of death or life.'

This passage shows the normal use of *xueqi* as a couple

and how it is very often linked with the earth. For instance, here we have the original and deep structure of life which is heavenly, and which is the 'supreme number' of the universe and the organization of cosmic life, made by the movement and interplay of *yin* and *yang*. In the human body it is called blood and *qi* because blood and *qi* are just the expression of the harmony of all this organization of life. It is also the way by which one may know if this person is in a good state, and if not, if the disease is serious. By observing the changing relationship of the two members of this couple we can see the general state of the living being, and see whether he is living his life according to the supreme numbers, which are just the principles of life.

Claude Larre: I wonder if people understand why the Chinese text looks at numbers? A number is an easy way to make distinction, and an easy way to make a composition. Numbers are not just a quantity, or a sequenced order, they can be used for combining and for distinguishing. When something is to do with heaven, its earthly counterpart is two. The union of one and two is perfect and necessary because if there is heaven it is just because there is earth, and likewise reciprocally. So numbers give this distinction and specification, this ability to join one with the other in order that their sum would be a sort of transfiguration of the nature of one and the other, or the accomplishment of one through the other. Heaven as just heaven is not very much, and earth restricted to its own nature would be nothing.

What is delicate, refined, subtle and nearly beyond expression in Chinese thinking is very much seen in the way they play with numbers. The supreme numbers, *zhi shu*, are no more or no less supreme than other numbers, but heaven and earth are supreme above all the 10,000 beings. So it is not only small numbers and big numbers which are used for heaven and earth. It is simply because you are talking of heaven and earth, which is the first distinction from the chaos, that you have to give the number a qualification at the level of heaven and earth. For this reason they call it a supreme number, *zhi shu*.

When they say 'the natural laws are a unity', they are insisting on the interaction of heaven and earth, and also on the necessity of heaven because of earth and earth because of heaven. So saying 'a single breath' is to go further than a simple addition. Heaven and earth are never added one to the other. They are united. The chaotic state from which heaven and earth are isolated is still there. It is important to understand that the function is at the level of life, but the analysis destroys the function in order to enable us to see the elements. It all has to be reunited one way or another to get back to the functioning. It is like a car. When your engine is running you cannot take it apart in order to see what piece is not working because when you do that the car stops. It is necessary to have the combination of the parts. And the more we are able to make sophisticated engines, the more very subtle little things there are, and if you touch one thing then everything stops. When there is some magic about the way things operate it means that the interconnection of things is so subtle that the functioning requires that everything is in the right place and goes at the right pace. Our trouble is that we want to understand how things work, but in so doing we destroy the movement itself. So many explanations are just in order to rebuild what has been destroyed by this single act of an analysis of life.

LING SHU CHAPTER 55

Ling shu chapter 55 says:

'The ebb and flow of the *qi* correspond with the *yinyang* of heaven and earth, with its four seasons and five elements. The increase in power and the decline of the *mai* are for the observation of emptiness and fullness, excess and insufficiency, in the blood and *qi*.'

Elisabeth Rochat: What is clear is that there are three levels. One is this kind of ebb and flow of *qi* in the universe for the interplay of *yin* and *yang* in the median space between heaven and earth, made by crossing and changing the four seasons and the five elements. This is all the internal structure of life. At the second level we have the earthly expression of that in the human body. This is all the variations of the couple blood and *qi*. That is perceptible and happening in and through and by the *mai*. After that we have the third level which is the level of human knowledge. This is to write books, to teach, to express in human language all the condition of life and health and disease.

That is very interesting for me because in other texts, especially from around the 3rd century BC, the ability to know is strongly linked to the quality and composition of blood and *qi*. For instance, if a being is not made of blood and *qi* he is unable to have what is called knowledge. In 'The Book of Rites' and in Xun zi, a great philosopher of the 3rd century BC, it is said that animals have knowledge and they have blood and *qi*. If you have a couple of birds, male and female, and one is killed, the other remains for a while just looking for his or her former companion. That is due to a certain knowledge which is not like human knowledge but which is a kind of memory and perception. This is due to the composition of the bird's blood and *qi*. This is the first step in the direction of the special quality of blood and *qi* which is used not only for nutrition and defence, but for much more than that.

Claude Larre: We understand that there is life in common between human beings and animals, and what is common is surely the blood and *qi* system. But there are different qualities of blood and *qi,* particularly at subtle levels. The communication and the common feeling between animal and man is enhanced by the familiarity of living in the same house, and being dependent upon one another. A gentleman's agreement is passed between animal and people for their survival, but the limit is the incompatibility of blood and *qi*. But if you give your blood to your cat, or if you take your cat's blood for the enriching of your own blood, they do not match. We know that immunity is the barrier and each would reject the other. So this is a question of blood, where blood is not blood because it is blood with *qi*. What is in common is the expression of life which is possible because there is blood and *qi*, but what is not in common is the fact that this blood and *qi* cannot mingle and give a positive result. Further analysis from a physical point of view is useless. Why certain animals are closer to us in their blood we can only know from experimentation, but from a philosophical point of view how that is possible I really have no answer.

SU WEN CHAPTER 54

Elisabeth Rochat: Su wen chapter 54 says:

'By the purpose (*yi* 意) which is natural to the human heart, man corresponds to the eight winds, and by his *qi* corresponds to heaven... By the blood and *qi* circulating in the *yin* and *yang mai*, he corresponds to the earth.'

The meaning of this is that the circulation of *yin* and *yang* (through the *yin* and *yang* meridians or *luo)* and the circulation of blood and *qi*, is in the likeness of earth, with all kinds of currents, rivers and valleys. This is better explained in Ling shu chapter 40 when the Yellow Emperor says:

'I learnt the correspondence between the 12 meridians (*jing mai* 經脈) and the 12 rivers (*jing shui* 經水).'

We can see that in both cases we have a regulation of animation by this character *jing* (經) which is meridian, but which is also all the norms or rules. The organization of this movement is expressed both in the network of animation and in the river. The chapter continues:

'So I know how each of them presents differences according to the five colours so that the clarity or turbidity are not the same. The blood and *qi* inside the man must be exactly the same thing. May I ask what exactly are the correspondences?'

The beginning of Qi Bo's answer is:

'The blood and *qi* in man are really analogous (to the earthly rivers). All that is under heaven forms a great unity. If that were not so, how would you explain all the diversity?'

If there is a real rule of life that we share, and if what we call the meridians are just the rule of life in our animation through blood and *qi*, we call this *mai*, and on earth we call it rivers. We observe the rivers on earth, and if we are right, what we have observed in the 12 rivers must also be true for our 12 meridians. For instance, these 12 rivers are not the same. Some are yellow, some have pure water. This is because what is forming these rivers is not the same. But if it is like that, and if all these 12 rivers have a different composition then the 12 meridians in man must also have fundamental differences. This would not be because of the composition of water and mud and so on, because here the variation is due to the composition of *xueqi*.

The Emperor understands that it is because of the differences that we can have the harmony, the unity. If all rivers were the same there would be no possibility of making the movement of life which is always present in exchanges and in separation, and in the diversity needed in order to reunite. The variety is able to make the composition, and the harmony of the composition is able to make a real living unity.

Guan zi chapter 39 says:

'What is water? It is the root of all things and the ancestral hall of all life. It is that from which beauty and ugliness, worthiness and unworthiness, stupidity and giftedness are produced.

'How do we know this to be so? Now the water of Qi is forceful, swift, and twisting. Therefore its people are greedy, uncouth, and warlike. The water of Chu is gentle, yielding, and pure. Therefore its people are lighthearted, resolute, and sure of themselves. The water of Yue is turbid, sluggish, and soaks the land. Therefore its people are stupid, disease ridden, and filthy. The water of Qin is thick like gruel and stagnant. It is obstructed, choked with silt, and wanders in confusion free of its banks. Therefore its people are greedy, violent, and deceptive, and they like to meddle in affairs. The water of Jin is bitter, harsh, and polluted. It is choked with silt and wanders in confusion free of its banks. Therefore its people are flattering and deceitful, cunning and profit seeking. The water of Yan collects in low places and is weak. It sinks into the ground, is clogged, and wanders in confusion free of its banks. Threfore its people are stupid, idiotic, and given to divination. They treat disease lightly and die readily. The water of Song is light, strong, and pure. Therefore its people are simple and at ease with themselves, and they like things to be done in the correct way. For this reason, the sages' transformation of the world lay in understanding water.' Guan zi chapter 39, translated by W.A. Rickett

This animation is very concrete, for instance in the irrigation of fields. But it is also reflected in the psychology of the people living in the country around this particular river. Guan zi here explains the psychology of people from different regions in China according to the differences in the composition of the rivers. We can see that if a man has strong *xueqi*, where he lives on earth the rivers will have the same strength. Both the psychology and the rivers have the same ability to express what is beyond, because you do not know if it is because the water is very muddy and the weather of the countryside is very wet that the people living there have a particular temper, or if it is because all the elements making life there create this kind of psychology in man and this kind of composition in the rivers. This comparison is not only in medical texts but is found in all classical literature.

By understanding a river we can have a better understanding of what *xueqi* is, and also what a meridian is in the human body. Perhaps a meridian is something which determines the composition of the *xueqi* of a territory, and this determines the quality of blood and the quality of irrigation and *qi* and so on of this whole territory of the body, from the depths to the superficial layers. The meridian is the acting ruler and maintainer of this composition which makes the quality of *qi* of this meridian by the particular composition of *xueqi*. That is enough to maintain the specific nature of an area of the body. It is the meridians which determine the life and composition of the texture of the flesh and the appearance of the skin, and of each territory of the body even if it is always just blood and *qi* which are circulating there. Just as on earth there is always water circulating.

SU WEN CHAPTER 27

The Su Wen, particularly in chapters 26 and 27, goes further. Chapter 27 emphasizes another kind of relationship in which the *yin* of the earth is the *jingshui* (經水) and the *yin* of man is the *jingmai* (經脈). It says that the effect of all the influences coming from the environment are analogous with the rivers on earth and the *jingmai* in man, and with all the circulation of *xueqi* in the body of man. So for instance, in winter when the weather is very cold the water freezes in the rivers, and this is a good example of what happens in man under an attack from cold. Of course the blood does not freeze exactly, but it is the same movement as in nature and we can easily see the effect of cold and warmth. It is the same mechanism which is at work in the human body when you are speaking of perverse cold or dryness and so on. The rivers and all the effects of the rivers throughout the surrounding territories are a good image of what can happen in the body. It is also the reason why they are often described with the same vocabulary, and sometimes it is very strange the way it translates into Chinese medical texts, for example to say the blood is frozen. The blood is not really freezing, but it is just a symbolic expression of this analogous process.

Going further in chapter 26 of Su wen we have other consequences of this classical analogy. If the meridian and the *xueqi* which is at work through the meridians, are sensitive in the same way that rivers are, they also have to follow all the circumstances of the environment, and not only cold or warmth but all natural cycles.

SU WEN CHAPTER 26

'In all acupuncture techniques one must first observe the *qi* of the sun and moon, of the planets and constellations, of the four seasons and eight regulators of time. Once this *qi* has been calculated one punctures. Thus when the weather is warm and the sun shines, man's blood is a rich liquid and the defensive *qi* is superficial. Then the blood disperses easily and the *qi* circulates easily. If the weather is cold and overcast, man's blood condenses and coagulates and the defensive *qi* is in the depths. When the moon begins to wax, blood and *qi* begin their vital development (*jing* 精) and the defensive *qi* begins to circulate. When the moon is full, blood and *qi* are in fullness, and the bulk of the flesh is solid. When the moon is empty (new moon), the bulk of the flesh weakens, the meridians and *luo* (絡) become empty, the defensive *qi* recedes and the bodily form alone remains.

'It is therefore according to the seasons of heaven (*tian shi* 天 時) that one regulates (*tiao* 調) blood and *qi*...This is why to maintain the life of the spirits (*yang shen* 養 神) it is necessary to know the state of repletion or emaciation of the body, the rising in power or the decline of the blood and *qi*, and of the nutrition and defence. The *xueqi* are the spirits of man, one cannot but pay great attention to their maintenance.'

Of course, you can needle even if you do not take exact account of all the circumstances of the sun and moon and so on. You are not obliged to know absolutely everything about universal science before you needle! But *xueqi* is constant through all the variations, and you can never reach the end of the variations because they are involved in all the cycles of the universe. When you take pulses for instance, you can feel and understand what is really happening in this living person. The variation in the *xueqi* in each meridian is like a theoretical expression of that. The assessment of this variation in the natural structure of man is made in order to understand the composition of this living being with all these aspects and differences. Thus we can see what the precise nature of *xueqi* is in one precise place at one precise moment of your development. This is also why we needle a particular point of a particular meridian rather than another one.

We also have to pay attention to the general variation of *xueqi* through the 12 meridians, according with the natural cycles. These natural cycles are cycles of the calendar and the unfolding of time. With the 12 rivers and 12 meridians we are in space, but you know that meridians are for time as well as space. They correspond to the 12 rivers and to the 12 months as far as the number 12 is concerned. But if we look at the solar calendar and all the planetary constellations, what does it all mean? It means that according to the position of the planets there is a special configuration revealing the particular quality of the influences coming from heaven. There would be the specific influence of the year or the month, and all the patterns in heaven made by the planets would give an indication of the general disposition of heaven during that time. Of course it is also always in perpetual movement, like heaven, and having an effect on the life of earth, as well as on the life of man. If there is an effect of this movement on life on earth it is distinct and normally perceptible in the movement within your vessels, your *xueqi*, and all the network of your animation. This is completely without pathology, it is just normal, even if it is so fine and subtle that it is very difficult to perceive. But if the patient has a real pathology this disturbance generally overrides all these very subtle cycles.

The 'eight regulators of time' are the eight great points of passage from one quality of time to another, and they are the beginning of the four seasons plus the two equinoxes and the two solstices, which are the points anchoring time during the year. They have several names but here they are called the *ba zheng* (八 正). We saw the character *zheng* in the discussion of *qi*, where it meant correct or regular.

Claude Larre: 'Regulator' is a way to express that there are eight special times where we have to be in correspondence with the seasons. So in the Chinese year where there are four seasons, which occurs nearly everywhere in China, the year is correct when the change of the season is marked or the apogee of the season is marked. They are called regulators of time because if these regular days are changed it means that the year is irregular, and what might be said for the year might also be said for an individual, because the year is a mass of *qi* which is regulated by the sun and moon, in the same way as man is a mass of *qi* which is regulated according to the cosmic year.

Elisabeth Rochat: Because of that we can have different pulses according to the seasons. In all the cycles of change and transformation which are difficult to see, we know by experience that the normal pulse is not the same in winter as it is in summer.

After that we have the variations, the adaptations in the *xueqi* according to the weather:

'When the weather is warm and the sun shines, man's blood is a rich humour and the defensive *qi* is superficial.'

Everything follows the *yang* movement which is stimulated inside the body and inside the *mai* and the spirits, because it is the same as in nature and the whole environment. For that reason everything rises up and diffuses a little bit more than usual. But if you needle with dispersion it is very easy because everything is at the edge and eager to go out, and you have to pay attention to that. On the contrary when the weather is cold and overcast as in winter you have the opposite effect. The same stimulation which is felt in nature is felt in the spirit of man giving order to your life. Man's blood condenses and coagulates like a river. It is not a stagnation in this case, it is only a stagnation if there is some disorder. This is why the pulse shows the difference between summer and winter. It is the obedience of the *xueqi* to the natural movement.

The passage goes on to discuss all the waxing and waning of the moon. If the sun has a special effect on the *qi*, the moon has a special effect on the liquids and water and blood. If the sea and the great mass of water obey the moon in a kind of regular movement, there is also a kind of reaction by the liquid mass in the human body in response to the moon according to its phase. This is just an expression of the power of the moon on us. If the moon is new and not visible, there is nearly no power of attraction, but if the moon is full it is manifesting its power of attraction. It is this kind of imperceptible but real tide within the human body which is perceptible in and through the *xueqi*.

'When the moon begins to wax, blood and *qi* begin their vital development (*jing* 精) and the defensive *qi* begins to circulate. When the moon is full, blood and *qi* are in fullness, the bulk of the flesh is solid.'

This is considered high tide, which is the fullness of the power.

'When it is new moon the bulk of the flesh weakens, the meridians and *luo* become empty, the defensive *qi* leaves, the bodily form alone remains.'

The power of the influence on the *xueqi* is not so strong at the new moon. This is the reason why some schools of acupuncture forbid needling at the new moon or the full moon.

Claude Larre: You cannot benefit someone if you are hesitating in what you are doing. So it is better to do something which is unorthodox only if you have a good reason. But if you hesitate just because of what is said by other people, you will never get anywhere because experience, feeling, obtaining *de qi* (得 氣) are of the essence, and knowing the book is secondary to getting the *qi*.

Elisabeth Rochat: All this is just to show how the great movement of the universe has a natural reflection in the *xueqi*, because the *xueqi* of man is the reflection of the harmonious composition, and what we call the harmonious composition is not only the mixing of liquids and currents of *qi*, but is far more than that. It is the way to follow the *yinyang* of nature which is in perpetual adaptation to the situation or to space and time.

SU WEN CHAPTER 17

At the beginning of chapter 17 of Su wen it says:

'The best method for palpation (of the pulse) is to do it at dawn: the *yin qi* is not yet in motion, the *yang qi* is not yet dispersed, food and drink have not yet penetrated, the meridians have not yet risen in power, the *luomai* (絡脈) are also steady, *qi* and blood are not yet in disorder. This is why one can then observe through palpation the faults of the pulse.'

Dawn is the only time when your *xueqi* is submitted to the circumstances of the surrounding environment and not disturbed by your own activity. We saw that there is already a lot to be obeyed in all the cycles of the universe. Now we have to add something else, which is our own normal activity during the day. Dawn is the moment when the defensive *qi* is returning to the surface, it is no longer completely in the depths, but it is not yet too active at the exterior. Dawn is also the period between day and night when the spirits are at peace, perhaps after the reconstitution of the night when the blood is stored in the liver giving the richness to the five *zang*. All that allows us to return to ourselves.

There are a lot of allusions in Chinese literature, for instance in Mencius, to this period of the dawn when we are able to see clearly what we are and what our life and our destiny is.

'In the calm air of the morning, just between night and day, the mind feels in a degree those desires and aversions which are proper to humanity, but the feeling is not strong, and it is fettered and destroyed by what takes place during the day.' Mencius chapter 6, section 1, part 8, translated by J. Legge.

It is the same thing with some of our great French poets. It is too true experientially not to have been noticed by a lot of clever people. This is also an effect of the *xueqi*.

Claude Larre: They say 'calm dawn' on purpose. They characterize dawn as a moment when everything stands still, in yourself and outside. Of course at that time there was not so much noise in the form of planes, cars, and so on!

Elisabeth Rochat: The characters for dawn are *ping dan* (平旦) in this text. *Dan* is the dawn, with the image of the rising sun above the horizon. *Ping* means well regulated, well balanced, at peace and calm, because everything is evenly distributed. The dawn therefore has the idea of calmness because all is equal, yet with an idea of richness. A calm abundance. You know that in the 19th century a great uprising occurred in China, the name of which was Taiping. This was a manifestation for the 'great peace'.

It is very difficult after dawn to see exactly how I am in my inner balance according to all the subtle influences and cycles of my position in the universe. If I eat, the simple fact of my digestion changes something in my pulse. If I do not eat it will also show. We can see that the most simple and normal things are able to obscure part of the perception of the very subtle harmony.

What is also interesting here is that we have absolutely and completely the relationships between *qi* and blood and the *mai*. The *mai* are not only the vessels because they are also the absolute conjunction of *xueqi*.

'*Qi* and blood are not yet in 'disorder'.'

The disorder here is not pathological, the meaning is simply to manifest all its different aspects. This is the normal variation of the *xueqi*.

One of the greatest commentators, Zhang Jiebin, emphasized the fact that in addition to all this we also have to pay attention to the constitution of the individual. If the person is strong and tall, or small and weak, then the normal pulse and the normal balance of the *xueqi*, and the perception which we have of it will not be the same. A 'normal' pulse just does not exist. It is only how this particular person with his own particular nature is constituted now in this place. A normal pulse for a thin man could be a very seriously ill pulse for another person. According to Su wen chapters 54 and 18 you also have to take the person's age into account. That is said in Confucius's 'Analects' with application to the moral life. If you want to be a sage, you have to pay attention to the appropriate things in your young years and in your old age.

'A man who desires to be a sage has to take care of three things. In the young years when the *xueqi* is always in motion without any great stability, he has to be on his guard against the pleasures of the senses because he is more vulnerable to the attractions of external things and desires. When he is an adult the *xueqi* is in all its vigour, thus he has to avoid quarrels because of his strength. In old age when the *xueqi* is in decline he has to pay attention to the passion to acquire and keep.' Analects, chapter16, section 7, translated by J. Legge.

If the *xueqi* is in decline he cannot absorb too much, either in the mind or in the body, in food or in ideas or in the possession of things. Classical medical texts say exactly the same thing but with more physiological effects.

LING SHU CHAPTER 18

For instance in Ling shu chapter 18:

'Huangdi says: If old men do not sleep at night which *qi* is responsible? If strong young men do not sleep in the day which *qi* is responsible?

'Qi Bo answers: With regard to strong men, their *qi* and blood are in full power, their flesh is smooth, the *qi* flows freely, the circulations of nutrition and defence occur normally. This is why they are full of life and vitality in the day and they sleep well at night. As for old men, their *qi* and blood are in decline, their flesh dries out, their *qi* flows with difficulty. The *qi* of the five *zang* fight with each other because they are not sufficient. Their nutritive *qi* declines and the defensive *qi* fights with itself on the inside. This is why they are lifeless during the day because there are not enough essences, and they do not sleep at night.'

This is one example of the consequences of this great exchange of the movement of vitality between youth and old age. It is also a question of *xueqi* because the diminishing strength of the *zang* just makes the essences less rich. If there is difficulty transforming and assimilating, the blood is not so rich and so powerful, and the *qi* is not so strong or abundant. As a result the *xueqi* is not the same, and you cannot do the same things in the same way. The correct rhythm of life, for instance sleeping during the night and being awake during the day, is expressed in the *xueqi*, and the *xueqi* is like a reflection of all the perversions of that rhythm.

THE BALANCE OF BLOOD AND QI

SU WEN CHAPTER 24

Elisabeth Rochat: The different balance of blood and *qi* in the meridians is found in several chapters in the Nei jing: particularly in Su wen chapter 24 and in Ling shu chapters 65 and 78. You can see that it is always the same for the *yang*. Su wen chapter 24 says:

'*Tai yang* (太 陽) normally has much blood and little *qi*.
Shao yang (少 陽) normally has little blood and much *qi*.
Yang ming (陽 明) normally has much *qi* and much blood.
Shao yin (少 陰) normally has little blood and much *qi*.
Jue yin (厥 陰) normally has much blood and little *qi*.
Tai yin (太 陰) normally has much *qi* and little blood.'

The normal theoretical explanation of '*tai yang* normally has much blood and little *qi*' is that *tai yang* is the bladder and small intestines meridians. The blood depends on the *yin* and the *qi* on the *yang*. *Tai yang* is normally called the first *yang*, and *tai* has the meaning of powerful. The meaning of the expression *tai yang* is that the *yang qi* just reaches the supreme point, but when the *yang* reaches the ridge pole, at noon for instance, at that very moment the *yin* appears. The sunset at night begins at noon, and winter begins in the middle of summer at the solstice. If in appearance the *yang* is powerful and high, what is increasing in power is the *yin*. This is the reason why this text says that the *tai yang* has much blood and little *qi* because although the *yang qi* is really powerful it is at the supreme point of its power. It cannot grow in power. But the *yin* power is able to increase more and more. This is one classical explanation.

'*Shao yang* normally has little blood and much *qi*.'

Shao yang is the gallbladder and triple heater, but in *shao yang* what is *yang* is full of forces to come. This is exactly the contrary. You contain within you the power of something which has not yet manifest. This is the reason why the power and the *qi* of *shao yang* are without limit because it is just beginning.

'*Yang ming* normally has much *qi* and much blood.'

This is because *yang ming* is the stomach and large intestine, and the stomach and *yang ming* are the source for blood as well as for *qi*, the sea of liquids and grains and so on. It is the total expression of the power of renewal, and the sea for the five *zang* and the six *fu*. Therefore the stomach meridian must have much blood and much *qi* at the same time. The abundance and richness of the effect are in the *ming*. This *yang ming* meridian is all the brilliance and the effect of the *yang*, but it is also on the chest and the abdomen - on the front *yin* part of the body, next to the *yin* meridians. It is also for the nourishment of the innermost part, for the blood and *qi* and the *zangfu*. In *yang ming* we have the richness of all the effects of all sorts of harvests.

With the *yin* it is more difficult and I think less interesting than for the *yang*. If it was really useful and if it had a real practical effect the texts would have to agree. With *shao yin* what is interesting is that we have another example of the fecundity of the *yin*.

'*Shao yin* normally has little blood and much *qi*.'

This is the contrary of *tai yang*. If *shao yin* represents the winter and *tai yang* the summer, then *shao yin* is the beginning of the increasing of the power of the *qi*. But in Ling shu chapter 65 it says '*shao yin* normally has much blood and little *qi*.' In this case the *shao yin* is the opposite of the *shao yang*. Both situations are possible because we know that the development of life is quite visible in the *yang* movement. It is normal to begin with the *yang*, with the thing which is full of the growing power, and all the effects of that. As far as the *yin* is concerned it is not the same. Is what we call *tai yin* the maximum of the *yin* or the *tai*(太), the greatest extension of the substantial manifestation within the *yin*? They are not the same thing. *Tai yin* could be autumn or winter. Autumn because this power is visible even if it is in the *yin*. It is just like the harvest in the fields. Up to late summer there is the effect of the growing and ripening of the crop, but after late summer that is finished. You have something which is full and you just have to cut it. If we are thinking of this aspect of richness we can call *tai yin* the autumn because there is a kind of power visible in the form of grains and fruits and so on. But if I am sensitive to the beginning of the *yin* movement which is a withdrawal, I can call autumn the *shao yin,* the young *yin.*

'*Jue yin* normally has much *qi* and little blood.'

This is because *jue yin* is the turning back. It is exactly like the new moon. In French we have two expressions for the same thing, the 'new moon' or the 'black night'. With the expression 'new moon' there is no moon, but we know that it is the beginning of something. The characters for *jue* (厥) and new moon (*shuo* 朔) have an element in common. It means a repeated attack against something because there is a resistance (cf Wieger Lesson 102D). On the right side of *jue* (厥) the character *qian* (欠) has a first meaning of a breath or lack of breath, and if you combine it with the element on the left side you have the meaning of hiccup, or a kind of suffocation, because this is the image of a breath having a kind of resistance. The part on the left of *jue* (厂) means a steep slope or a cliff, like a piece of rock. Wieger says of *jue* that you are out of breath because ascending this cliff is very hard. In classical Chinese this character is usually used as a pronoun. But what is more interesting is the relationship with other characters such as *ni* (逆), which is a countercurrent. Very often this is used with a negative meaning because it is to not respect the natural rhythm. But it can also be the normal ebb and flow.

LING SHU CHAPTER 65

Ling shu chapter 65:

'Huangdi asks: Women do not have beards. Could they not have blood and *qi?*'

'Qi Bo answers: *Chong mai* (衝 脈) and *ren mai* (任 脈) both arise in the middle of the intimate envelope, *bao zhong* (胞 中). They rise up the back on the inside and make the sea of *jingluo*. Their pathways emerge and run along the abdomen on the right side and rise up. They meet together at the pharynx. A detachment (*jie* 別) takes a connecting relationship with the lips and the mouth. When blood and *qi* rise in power the skin is humidified and the flesh is warmed. When only the blood rises in power, drop by drop in the area of the skin it gives what is necessary for the growth of hair. Women in their natural physiology have an excess of *qi* and an insufficiency of blood following the frequent loss of blood. *Chong mai* and *ren mai* do not make her mouth and lips flourish, and because of this they do not have a beard growing there.'

There is a difference in the way blood and *qi* make life in the physiology of men and women. This difference is quite original because it is under the authority of the extraordinary meridians, and the extraordinary meridians are generally the first model for the structure of the human body. *Ren* and *chong mai* are both very important in gynaecology, in defining the special way the *xue* and *qi* work in the body of a woman. It is not the same as in a man. Another aspect of this difference is perceptible in the beard because the *xueqi* gives life and for a man it is visible at the top of the body in a kind of richness arising and making the vegetation flourish! But for a woman there is another way to make life powerful, and they have menstruation and the ability to nourish a child through this *xueqi* and its particular use in the woman's intimate envelope, *bao* (胞), which takes the form of the uterus. The meaning of *bao* in the case of a woman can be uterus, just as the *jing* (精) is a general reality but for a man can have the specific meaning of sperm. It is all according to context.

What is interesting to know is that there is a definite difference in the sexes. The *qiao mai* (蹻 脈) are involved in the process, but the difference is visible in the different functioning of the blood and *qi*. Later on in the text Huangdi is a little bit forward in asking about the particular case of natural and accidental eunuchs. There something is changed or is not normal in the primitive regulation of vitality expressing itself inside and by the *xueqi*.

'In eunuchs, by accident or operation, their ancestral muscle has gone, their *chong mai* has been attacked, the blood has been dispersed without return. The skin is knotted on the inside. There is no flourishing at the lips and mouth and this is why the beard does not grow.'

Of course it is not a simple loss of blood, it is something definitely changed, altered in the way of ruling the *xueqi*. The result is visible on the skin and the beard and so on. There is no flourishing at the lips and mouth, and this is why the beard does not grow.

'With natural eunuchs there is an insufficiency in their nature, *tian* (天). With them *chong mai* and *ren mai* have not risen in power, the ancestral muscle is not achieved (*bu cheng* 不 成). They have *qi* but no blood.'

This is another way of saying that something is wrong in the natural composition of the *xueqi*. Something very original and primitive in the constitution of the embryo and in the differentiation of the sex, and all the ways by which these influences and this composition is working, is not the same. Knowing that, all the renewal of the *xueqi* comes from posterior heaven.

THE ORIGINS OF BLOOD AND QI

LING SHU CHAPTER 10

Elisabeth Rochat: In the beginning of Ling shu chapter 10 it says:

'When a human being begins life, first the essences are perfectly composed (*cheng* 成). When the essences are thus perfectly composed, brain and marrow are produced (*sheng* 生), the bones form the framework, the *mai* nourish, the muscular forces give the hardness, the flesh gives the compartments, the layers of the skin are firm and body hair and head hair grow in length. The grains enter the stomach, the ways of animation (*mai dao* 脈 道) establish free circulation and blood and *qi* then circulate.'

There is a kind of growth and movement of life making the body, making the embryo up to the point of birth. After that, what is important is the way in which you are able to manage your own life by receiving all that comes from outside, and assimilating it into the structure of your body which is already complete. This is the difference between blood and *qi* and *jing*. *Jing* is more on the side of life and the process of the development of life itself, and blood and *qi* are rather this composition which is able to receive and to reflect all the conditions of life and all its variations. This is a theoretical difference because everything which comes from the stomach is also *jing*. But there is in the essences a part which is original and from anterior heaven. There is no original *xueqi*, even if its regulation is inscribed in the individual nature of each person. This circulation is your animation, and your animation is also how you adapt to and reflect all the surrounding environment and everything which happens inside you.

LING SHU CHAPTER 60

Ling shu chapter 60 says:

'The stomach is the sea of *qi* and blood coming from liquids and grains. The clouds and *qi* which come from this sea circulate everywhere under heaven. The *qi* and blood that come from the stomach form the trenches of the meridians (*jing sui* 經 隧).'

We saw previously what it means to be a sea, and here we

have another good explanation of it. The stomach is a sea of *qi* and blood coming from the liquids and grains because from the stomach we have the releasing which allows the renewal of essences and *qi* leading to the composition and recompostion of *xueqi*. At the same time the stomach also receives all kinds of essences and forces needed to continue its work. For instance the liquids of the stomach and the *yang* of the stomach enable it to transform and to distribute throughout the body with the help of the spleen.

What is also interesting is this idea of trenches or tunnels, the *jing sui* (經 隧). You know that it is said that the blood circulates inside the meridians and the *qi*, or the defensive *qi* in particular, circulates outside of them. This is one view which is better applied to the defensive and nutritive forces, even if in this case they are not completely separate. I think everything relies on the understanding of this character for meridian, *jing* (經).

With this image of the 'trenches of meridians' we have a bit of an explanation. If the meridian is what lies behind all that is passing through these valleys, we have the direction, the regulation and the commanding point for all the effects, but we do not have one particular vessel or one particular location. The meridian is in the depths because it is commanding from the inside and is related to the *zang* of the interior. But what is it, and what is the materialization of the meridian, and what is the materialization of blood and *qi?* This is the question.

In a valley we have a river and the river is real. We can touch the water. But the effect of the valley and the river is not only the water but a certain quality of water, and also a certain quality of vegetation and fertility due to the irrigation by the water and the regularity of the flow or lack of flow of this water from the source. Life inside this valley is dependent on the general relief, and that is influenced by what is behind the river. In the body we can have one blood vessel, or two or none. This is not the problem. This is not the meridian. The meridian is behind the blood vessel, it is behind all the perceptible effects on this precise territory of the body.

All kinds of things pass through the river. There is not only water flowing but also boats and roads and trains and so on. That all makes up life, nutrition and defence. The image of a trench is quite good for that. It contains the idea of all these kinds of receptacles with a lot of passages and a lot of effects. Never forget that the effects of the passage manifest themselves in other ways, and a meridian is just able to control that, perhaps because of having created it. What is the strength which makes this river flow for the first time through this mountain? We do not know exactly, but there is something which is just there, and which is more the meridian than anything else. Even if sometimes we can see that there is a blood vessel or a nerve.

Claude Larre: A big company has a so-called organic nature, involving the organization of power and services from the president down to the door keeper. This has been thought up by a person knowing that direction, efficiency and control have to be organized in order to produce whatever is wanted. It is done in a way that can be controlled and added to, and benefits your financial investment because it is invested in the organism.

Usually in our Western view of medicine we call the organism the flesh, the bones, the organs and everything which we can see and touch. But if we take this organism at the level of what is necessary for having an effect, we know that there are real lines of power, because if we change one director for another one it may not make any difference to the running of the company. But if you suppress anything in the organism then everything will collapse.

So we know the difference between an organism which is directing things and the person in charge of that directing. We are not looking here for any particular tangible sign, it is the blood and the *qi* itself which are organized and the meridian is just this string of power. So when this passage talks about trenches, it is just that there is a place where things are organized for effect. We can reduce the area of a meridian to that. If we were only speaking materially, this would be enough to explain it, but it has to account for the energy of life. We go quite a long way in the direction of materialization with the *jing*, which is the same character as is used for the five classics (*wu jing* 五 經). Of course they are books, but it is not just their content which is interesting, it is the direction which they take for organizing life from the Chinese point of view. Without a place for organizing there is no enterprise and no people. But the organization is never the people who are organized.

Elisabeth Rochat: This image of the five classics is interesting because there were a lot of people who worked carefully on these texts. The five classics were simply the expression of life in a certain part of the world. After that they became books which could be touched and read. But their effects were not visible because effects are not only in the classroom. Children learnt these classics by heart. There was also the individual work in the mind of each person involved with them, and all of that is like a releasing. Just as blood is not only the materialization of the blood, but whatever is released from it.

In the valley we have a river, and the water in the river by virtue of its density and richness lies on the bottom of the valley and flows there and not on the top of the mountain. The materialization of water, which is this kind of essential element of life, is really more visible in the valley.

SU WEN CHAPTER 21

Su Wen chapter 21 says:

'The *qi* of the solid food penetrates the stomach; there is diffusion of essences to the liver and impregnation of *qi* to the musculature. The *qi* of the solid food penetrates the stomach. The unclear *qi* (*zhuo qi* 濁 氣 - clear *qi* coming from food) is transferred to the heart, there is impregnation of essences to the network of animation (*mai* 脈). The *mai* flow to the meridians. The *qi* of the meridians is transferred to the lung. The lung receives the 100 *mai* in audience. They transport the essences to the skin and body hair. Body hair and *mai* join their essences and there is circulation of the *qi* to the residence (*fu* 府). The essences that are in the residence are the radiant spirits (*shen ming* 神 明). They dwell in the four other *zang*. Their *qi* is referred to the arbiter judge (*quan heng* 權 衡). The arbiter judge must be equitable and the mouth of *qi* (*qi kou* 氣 口) perfectly formed at the pulse (*cun* 寸). Thus there is estimation (of the diagnosis) of death or life.'

This is the first part of the quotation. After that there is a presentation of the liquid foods organizing and renewing the bodily fluids. What is interesting here is that you can see an alternation of essences and *qi* in the text. This couple make the movement of the text, even in an English translation. It shows how *qi* and essences just arise one from the other.

In the first part of the passage the emphasis is on animation and the pulse, and the strength of all circulation. In the third sentence the 'unclear *qi*' is nothing other than the pure juice, rich in essences, which is able to pass through the diaphragm and make the substance of the blood. It is unclear not because it is unclean, but because it is coming from food and not from respiration.

'The unclear *qi* is transferred to the heart, there is impregnation of essences to the network of animation.'

What is the meaning of that? After the passage through the heart there is blood, and this blood is nothing other than essences in the special form of essences making the network of animation. This is all the *xuemai* (血脈), all the circulation of blood through the network of animation under the authority of the heart. Through these essences and through this blood we have at the same time the precious impulse given by the heart to this circulation through the *mai*. 'The *qi* of the *mai* flows to the meridians' is just a way of saying that it is submitted to the great rule of life of circulation and animation. It is not just pushed, it is obeying the route which is the meridians.

'The *qi* of the meridians is transferred to the lung. The lung receives the 100 *mai* in audience.'

This is also the sea of *qi* in the middle of the chest, with all kinds of *qi* in the body obeying the ancestral *qi.* Blood is able to master the *qi* of the body. Blood is able to order the regulation of this circulation, and here it is said that the function of the lung is to receive the 100 *mai* in the dawn audience. This is the only moment when it is possible to regulate absolutely.

'It transports the essences to the skin and body hair.'

From the lung all this *xueqi, yin* and *yang* increase and force their way through all the meridians, and are distributed and propagated up to the skin and body hair under the authority of the lung.

'Body hair and *mai* join their essences.'

This is a way to express that the power of the *qi* and the blood, and the lungs and the heart are all joined together. The *mai* are under the special authority of the heart, and the skin and body hair are under the special authority of the lungs. This is a mixing of *xueqi* and everything under the authority of lungs and heart.

'And there is circulation of the *qi* to the residence (*fu* 府).'

The *fu* (府) here is not one of the six fu, it is the middle of the chest. This is the special centre of vitality linked with the influences coming from the heart.

'The essences that are in the residence are the radiant spirits. They dwell in the four other *zang*.'

If the *xueqi*, the heart and the lungs are functioning well, and all the meridians and the *zangfu* are in harmony with this functioning, there is a kind of concentration of perfect *xueqi* at this place, and there is a good impregnation of the layers of the skin. The eyes and vision are good, and the brain is alert. The bones are solid. All that is called *shen ming*. At the same time the blood and the essences of the blood, carried on by good *qi*, are also able to make the life of the spirits, and to make the vital spirits which are the *jingshen*. 'They dwell in the four other *zang*' because if what is coming from the depths of the heart, this real deep and true vitality, is strong enough, there is an effect in what is animated from inside the other *zang*. In each *zang* there is this same vitality, *jingshen*, which rules the functioning, and through that creates not only good vision in the eyes but also this kind of real perception and knowledge of things.

'Their *qi* is referred to the arbiter judge.'

The 'arbiter judge' (*quan heng* 權衡) here is a way to refer to the taking of the pulses which are at the end of the *mai*. We know that this *xueqi* is not only coming from food through the stomach and from the lungs and the heart, but is also a mirror of the inner animation by each *zang*. The meaning is that with the pulse we have not only the perception of what is wrong perhaps in the fire of the liver or this countercurrent here, but we can reach down to the spirit of this person. Because sometimes, although I do not know how because I am also a being made from *xueqi* and spirit and *jingshen*, we can touch something else and can feel or know things which we are unable to explain by other means.

Quan heng (權 衡) is also linked with the four seasons traditionally speaking, for instance at the end of Huainan zi chapter 5:

'For the government of spring, adopt the compass. For the government of autumn, adopt the square. For the government of winter, adopt the weight (*quan* 權). For the government of summer, adopt the balance-beam (*heng* 衡).'

Etymologically speaking *heng* represents part of a balance, and a beam in a scale. The use of this character is sometimes linked to the four seasons which are also the beam in the scale or the balance for the year.

Quan had a special meaning in the Legalist School, and was one of the main terms they used. It is the power, the authority, especially of a prince. I think that it is that the pulse is seen here as a manifestation of what is really happening in the body. It is the function of the constant rule of life, and the perpetual adaptation to make this rule efficient. In the pulse there is something which is constant but which is never the same, and this is perhaps the reason why they chose these two characters, *quan heng*, to manifest this double aspect or two-fold quality of each pulse at each moment. But it is also a very general expression, and common even in classical Chinese with the simple meaning of a judge or to be able to give a judgment. Here you are able to view like a practitioner, to make judgments.

Claude Larre: It seems to me that there may have been a derivation of meaning from more simple tools like the water level and the plumb line. If you know how to make an horizontal and a vertical perfectly, then you know how to place things exactly. But those are ordinary things. If you can combine them with in this case the scale and balance, then it is more representative of the quality. If you use both principles there is some sort of integration of one system with another to make the right decision. Because how a thing which is used at one level is transferred to another level and what the transformation for that transferral is, is something which is possible only if you look across many texts in order to know the evolution of the meaning.

Question: The lungs are sometimes described as a judge, is this the same term or a different one?

Elisabeth Rochat: The arbiter judge must be the same thing. I think it is also the idea that it has to be unbiased. The judge and the pulses have to be pure and equal. But within the equality there is always variation. It is the same as the situation at dawn.

'The arbiter judge must be equitable and the mouth of *qi* perfectly formed at the pulse, thus there is estimation of death or life.'

The real orientation is life, and through the *xueqi* you have the realisation and the orientation of the *mai*.

BLOOD AND QI, SPIRIT AND QI

LING SHU CHAPTER 3

Elisabeth Rochat: Next we have a series of texts which emphasize the life of the spirits and the expression of that life through the *shenming*. For example in Ling shu chapter 3 we see:

'"The crude (practitioner) observes the body." This means that he observes the techniques of puncturing. "The superior (practitioner) observes the spirits." This means that he observes the blood and *qi* of man, tonifying or dispersing, following excess or deficiency.'

What is interesting here is the near equality of identity

between the spirits and blood and *qi*. Blood and *qi* are one of the best ways through which the spirits express themselves in a perceptible way. It is perceptible because it is always through the balance of *xueqi* that we have the indication for treatment. You know if there is excess or deficiency, so you tonify or disperse.

SU WEN CHAPTER 26

At the end of Su wen chapter 26 we have the following:

'This is why in order to maintain the life of the spirits, *yang shen* (養 神), it is necessary to know the state of repletion or emaciation of the body, the rising in power or the decline of the blood and *qi* of nutrition and defence. The blood and *qi* are the spirits of man, one cannot but pay great attention to their maintenance.'

Here we can clearly see the equivalence between blood and *qi* and the spirits of man, *xue qi zhe ren zhi shen* (血 氣 者 人 之 神). But they are not exactly the same thing. If you want to perceive something of the state of the spirits or their expression, because the spirits themselves are beyond any analysis by logical means, you have to observe the state of the *xueqi*, and this is perceptible in the general state of the body. Is this person in a state of good balance, is there is a good current of rich liquids circulating in the bulk of the flesh? If there is, then the flesh is firm and the skin is supple and solid. If not, then there is something wrong in the *xueqi*, in the circulation or the richness of the circulation and so on. That is a sign that there is something wrong with what finally determines the condition of that circulation or the *xueqi*, which is the spirits.

On the other hand, if the *xueqi* for one reason or another is too weak, there is something wrong in the means offered to the spirits to express themselves. It can begin with something wrong in the spirits, or emotions, and as a result, little by little, something goes wrong in the harmonious composition of the *xueqi*. If something is wrong in the composition of the *xueqi* there is a countercurrent, because if the mass of the blood is too heavy there may be stagnation, or if the liquids are not enough, or if the *qi* has too much impulse, there can be a countercurrent or hesitation with all kinds of disorder.

If for any external reason, perhaps because the defence or the nutrition is not strong enough, an attack comes from the exterior and leads to a disease in which there is an imbalance in the *xueqi*, that will also lead to a lack of expression of the spirits, according to Su wen chapter 21. The *xueqi* nourish the spirits in order to inspire their life expressed through the five *zang*.

LING SHU CHAPTER 18

Ling shu chapter 18 has another formulation of the same idea:

'Huangdi: Blood and *qi* under different names are of the same type. How is this?

'Qi Bo: Nutrition and defence are *jingqi* (精氣), as for the blood it is *shenqi* (神氣). This is for the reason that blood and *qi* have different denominations while being of the same type.'

Here the difference between nutrition and defence and *xueqi* is clearly stated. With nutrition and defence we have all the interplay of essences and *qi* making the strength in the muscles and the circulation. But with *xueqi* we have something else. We have the expression of the depths of the heart through the blood and the animation of the network and also the best way to store essences, nourish the spirit and have a real spiritual life. The level of *xueqi* is where there is perpetual adaptation and the presence of the spirits, and you know that the spirits are the real inspiration for exchanges and transformation for life. That is said in chapter 9 of Su wen, when the heart is described as the trunk of life and the dwelling place for all transformations made under the influence of the spirits. This is definitely the difference between blood and other liquids.

Because of *xueqi* having the power and the presence of the spirits, there is this communication with the outside which is linked to knowledge, not only through the orifices, but also through all the sensations that we can have such as pain, cold, itching and so on. These are due to the circulation and presence of *xueqi* everywhere, but also because there is this special movement to and from the heart by the spirits, whose presence is the necessary condition for the perception which is really knowledge, and which is not just an instinctive reaction without consideration. For instance, a disturbance of the couple *xueqi* would lead to *jing* (驚), starting with fright or surprise. This would then lead to a lack of the presence of the spirits, and if something then happened at the level of the skin or one of the orifices, there would not be a good reaction because of this lack of spirits due to the disorder in the animation.

In 'The Book of Rites' it says that man is composed of *xueqi* and has knowledge coming from the heart. This is the double nature of man. Afterwards the text continues by describing the possibility of emotional expression, because we are sensitive to exterior influences on all this *xueqi* as reflected in the spirit of the heart. This is the reason why we have to know how to conduct our life following the art of the heart, *xin shu* (心 術). Further on it is written that if blood and *qi* are in harmonious and well balanced composition, *he ping* (和 平), then the example of good people becomes stronger and conduct is rectified.

Another quotation from Xun zi says:

'All living creatures between heaven and earth, which have blood and *qi* must possess consciousness, and nothing that possesses consciousness fails to love its own kind.' Xun zi chapter 19, translated by Burton Watson

If you take all the living beings between heaven and earth, those of them which have blood and *qi* also necessarily have consciousness. This is the kind of quotation which you can find in other books too. It is just to emphasize this intimate relationship between these things, and why it is not only the nutrition and defence that you judge.

Question: Could you talk about the relationship of the blood with the *hun* (魂)?

Elisabeth Rochat: The *hun* are the most specific aspect of the spiritual animation of the imagination and knowledge and all kinds of intelligence and cleverness. These kind of spirits, *shen* or *hun*, need rich, clear and pure essences to best express themselves. Through the *hun* we are able to have imagination and to see what the right way to understand something is. This is seen during the day through the spirit of the heart, but during the night when the blood is specifically filling the liver, the *hun*, which depend and dwell in the liver, are full of this power of the essences made by the blood. At that time they express their ability to know and to discern, to be clear and to form images, in the interior, and we have dreams for instance. If we are in good health these dreams are just the result of this discernment and production of images natural to the *hun*. This is a special nightly activity of the *hun*. During the day the *hun* follow the *shen*. All that is due to the essences of blood and *qi*.

If I want to see something well, I have to make an effort and to expend a certain amount of blood, not only for the optic nerve and the system of the eyes, but also in order to understand what I am reading or whatever. We know that when we look at a patient it can be an effort not only to see what the problem really is but also to see what the meaning of it is. Very often this is an unconscious process, but it is effective. Normally there is no difference between *shen* and *hun* in a healthy man.

Question: I have a question related to what you were saying before about the *yuan* (原, sources). The idea of the yellow sources *huang quan* (黃 泉) has been mentioned, is there more information about them?

Claude Larre: Mythologically speaking they are physical, but mythology is just a way to talk of life and to initiate an approach to its meaning. If the sources are connected with earth then their colour is yellow. The yellow of the sources means that whatever the influence of heaven might be there can be no actual real man standing on earth unless he is made with material from the earth. Everywhere everybody has a connection with the earth, and the source of life is found in the depths of the earth where water is present.

You may take this physically, mythologically or psychologically. It is not from mythology itself that you can understand mythology, it is from your own life. You come from earth, and on earth the influence from heaven circulates in a form more materialized by water than by air. It is not wrong to see air circulating inside the pulse, but it might be more correct to see the circulation of the power of heaven as liquid.

Yin and *yang* are the limit of the understanding of life because at the highest level of abstraction they are the container of life. You may take *yinyang* as an idea, a symbol, or a representation in a boundless world. You cannot speak of man and his destiny unless you speak of *yin* and *yang* in the process of crossing. This is so essential that we understand all books and all treatises could not start with anything other than *yinyang*. The yellow sources are the beginning of *yin* and *yang*. *Yin* and *yang* are understood by what happens there, although there is no localization as such.

There are nine sources because everything which is big and large and without very much specification is represented by nine. There are nine territories for us and nine ways to be liberated in heaven, and there are nine ways for water. Maybe in certain texts there are 27 abysses because three times nine is 27. The flexibility of the text is such that you may understand what they say but you cannot deduce anything from what you understand! You understand something, and then you understand something else, and if you want to put that all together it is your decision, but it is not the Chinese conclusion. They give you the pieces of the riddle and you build what you want from them. But the pieces which are given are given in a certain definite form, so it is not vague. The yellow sources are just there, and there is some organizational power which is of a very low level. And the place where life insists on taking its form is in water.

The origin of man may be heaven and earth but if we want to contact that we have to go to a more specific level. We go through rites of death and extend ourselves to our ancestors, and see how the 10,000 beings are just the crossing of *yin* and *yang* which incorporates the meeting of life. We see in Ling shu chapter 8 that what has been built is *ying qi* (營氣) and this is just *qi* naturally coming to its place. Without *ying qi* we could not really understand what life is. If it was not a natural building, then it would not be necessary to nourish it again and again, because life is in the building.

The act of life is to be building. People who do not take care of themselves are not really living. But at the same time life in the open has to be protected and the marvellous thing is that when we are nourishing we are also protecting, and when we are protecting we are saving what will be necessary to rebuild our life.

INDEX

INDEX